Jack Berens

Jack Berens has always had a special interest in electronics and communications. In addition to his experience as an electronics engineer, he has also been an instructor at the Delehanty Institute in New York, where he taught theory and servicing of radio and television communications equipment. He owned and managed the Eveready Service Company, which serviced and maintained electronics equipment. Mr. Berens is a co-author of *Getting Started in Amateur Radio* and *Building the Amateur Radio Station.*

Stephen Berens

Stephen Berens, like his father Jack, has always held a keen interest in electronic theory and equipment. He graduated from Rensselaer Polytechnic Institute in 1966, and since that time has worked for Sperry Gyroscope as an engineer supervising radar equipment and traffic control. He is presently employed at United States Electronics Publications doing technical writing as a project engineer.

Cover Design by Arnold Breisblatt

Understanding and Troubleshooting Solid-State Electronic Equipment

Understanding and Troubleshooting Solid-State Electronic Equipment

Jack Berens and Stephen Berens

CHILTON BOOK COMPANY

Philadelphia   New York   London

Acknowledgments

Our deepest appreciation goes to Gloria Berens, wife and mother, for her constant understanding and aid, and to Dr. Joseph Vogelman for his very able and timely assistance in preparing the manuscript.

Jack Berens
Stephen Berens

Contents

CHAPTER I

Introduction

One of the greatest developments in the electronics industry in the last 25 years has been the introduction of the transistor. When this tiny solid-state device was developed by Bell Telephone Laboratories, very few people foresaw the role that the transistor would play in today's electronics industry. Who would have thought that this little semiconductor device would have such phenomenal growth? Who could conceive the revolution it would cause in the electronics industry?

The performance of the transistor, when first introduced, left much to be desired. Most early problems were caused by inadequate fabrication techniques. Also, manufacturers of tube-type equipment were reluctant to change over production-line assemblies. After all, no one wanted to spend money on a device that had not proved itself. Today, because of tremendously improved fabrication techniques, the solid-state device dominates the entire electronics industry. New concepts in the uses of this device have excited the electronics industry to the extent that not one manufacturer has been able to avoid its use. The reasons are obvious; the physical size and power requirements have shrunk to the point where the electronic giant of today requires only 1/100 the size and power of its vacuum-tube counterpart of 20 years ago. Thanks to improved fabrication techniques, transistors, semiconductor diodes, and associated components are being made up into modules called *integrated circuits* (*IC's*).

The IC's in Fig. 1–1, for example, are complete hybrid operational amplifiers.

Transistorized circuitry is now so commonplace that we can safely predict that very soon every piece of electronic equipment will be completely transistorized. There is no aspect of the electronics industry that has not felt the impact of the transistor.

In order to play a part in this growing industry, it is neces-

Fig. 1-1. NSC Type NS7560–NS7560A hybrid operational amplifiers.

sary to become completely familiar with the semiconductor device. This book has been written for those technicians and engineers who want to be able to service and maintain equipment utilizing these devices. Typical circuits will be examined, taken apart, and analyzed in simple, easy-to-understand language. The circuits included in this book are used in presently designed equipment—in radio transmitters, hi-fi and communication equipment, computers, test equipment, TV sets, and receivers.

Many circuits involving the use of transistors are standard. Thus, understanding how a circuit functions in one type of equipment will enable you to understand how it functions in many other types of equipment. This book is designed to be used by people whose technical background in electronics is not very extensive. As we delve into the understanding of these circuits, we will assist you in developing techniques in servicing and in discovering similarities in different equipment. For example, a voltage regulator circuit used in a transmitter can be slightly altered for use in a communications receiver. A speech amplifier circuit in hi-fi equipment can also be used, with slight modification, in a broadcasting station. So if you understand the workings of a transistorized circuit in a broadcasting station, this knowledge will enable you to understand how the same circuit functions in other related equipment. It is as simple as that.

Servicing equipment can be accomplished with little difficulty once you know how the transistor works. One defective transistor can shut down an entire computer complex until a technician can locate the defective stage. Although the computer is a giant and can extend into many cabinets, it can be conceived in sections down to its smallest component. In computer technology transistors are encompassed in modules. Whether you are working with a single transistor or one encompassed in a module, you will learn that the service approach is the same. Actually, the more you delve into it, the more you will discover that this transistorized module is duplicated in many other sections of the computer complex. If you examine the computer carefully, you will find many identical modules and printed circuits.

The use of transistors in TV sets is also growing rapidly in popularity. One major TV-set manufacturer announced recently that, within a few short years, the only tube in a TV set will be the picture tube. Imported, miniaturized TV sets are now flooding the market—and all of them are transistorized. Even the high-voltage rectifier tube can be replaced with a solid-state device!

Obviously, transistors and other semiconductor devices are beginning to dominate the electronics industry. If you want to succeed in this new industry, you must recognize the importance of understanding these devices. Transistor design requirements are more stringent than those for vacuum tubes. Therefore, a new approach to servicing is required which this book will make clear. It will illustrate how to develop a new concept in servicing these semiconductor devices and will explain a method of approach based on an understanding of the transistor. With a basic knowledge of the requirements and operation of the transistor, you should have no difficulty in servicing one of them—quickly and easily.

Sometimes, the small physical size of the equipment may be the only deterrent to a simple repair problem. A few manufacturers take advantage of the small size of the transistor to jam components into as small a space as possible. Thus, special problems are created for the serviceman. Specific servicing techniques must be developed to cope with situations arising when transistors have components or mechanical assemblies mounted around or over them. A good deal of ingenuity is required in order to test or repair these transistors and associated components successfully.

A vast array of specialized tools and test equipment is made for those who service transistorized equipment. Special soldering guns with interchangeable tips have a variety of applications. These special tips permit soldering, or "unsoldering," in otherwise inaccessible places. Test equipment specially designed for checking transistors and associated circuitry is also available.

In conclusion, let us state that the individual who takes the time to understand "what makes the transistor tick" will be the one who will be able to service it and will thus participate in and grow with this new development in the electronics industry.

CHAPTER II

Semiconductors

In order to understand a circuit using a semiconductor, it is useful to have some knowledge of the electrical and physical properties of the semiconductor device. In beginning this analysis, we will review the principles of the electron theory of matter.

THE ELECTRON THEORY OF MATTER

Almost all matter is composed of some combination of elements. The air we breathe, for example, consists of various combinations of the elements oxygen, nitrogen, hydrogen, helium, and others. If we could split the element of, let us say, hydrogen until we had the smallest amount of hydrogen that still retained the characteristics of hydrogen—physical, chemical, and electrical—we would be said to have an *atom* of hydrogen.

The atom is an elementary particle that was loosely conceived of by the Greek philosophers of about 4 B.C. It was not until the nineteenth century that the classical atomic theory was postulated by William Higgins and John Dalton. In the classical theory, the atom is described as having a nucleus containing one or more protons with electrons held in an orbit about the nucleus by the electrostatic force created by virtue of the positive charge(s) of the proton(s) in the nucleus and the negative charge(s) of the orbiting electron(s). An analogy can be made to the gravitational force of the solar system, although this is not strictly applicable. Such an analogy will, however, suffice for the classical representation of the atom.

The nucleus of the atom, in addition to possessing the positive charge, contains almost all the mass of the atom. Both an electron and a proton have equal but opposite charges (-1 and $+1$, respectively), but a proton weight about 1800 times more than an electron. It is also larger by the same amount. Essentially, an atom is an electrostatically neutral system. The atom itself has a net charge of 0 (zero).

When an atom gains or loses electrons, it is no longer electrically uncharged. If an electron is gained, the atom assumes a negative charge (-1 being assigned to an atom gaining one electron). If an atom loses an electron, the atom acquires a positive charge ($+1$ being assigned to an atom losing one electron). The loss or gain of one or more electrons can be achieved by strictly chemical means. Although protons can be removed from the nucleus of an atom, complex nuclear methods are necessary to achieve this result.

Atoms may combine to form *molecules*. A molecule is the smallest portion of a substance that is composed of the same kinds of atoms in the same proportion as the substance contains as a whole. Gases such as oxygen and nitrogen contain two atoms of the same kind per molecule of gas. Chemically, for example, a molecule of oxygen gas is written O_2. Since there are two atoms per molecule of oxygen gas, it is said to have *diatomic molecules*. Since there is only one kind of atom in oxygen gas (both are oxygen atoms), oxygen gas is also said to have *homatomic molecules*. Various elements reduce to molecules having more than one or two similar atoms per molecule. Phosphorous is composed of molecules having four atoms of phosphorous per molecule (chemically, P_4). It is also worth mentioning that *compounds* must be composed of two or more different kinds of atoms. Table salt, NaCl chemically, contains one sodium atom and one chlorine atom per molecule of salt. When a molecule contains two different kinds of atoms, such as NaCl, it is said to be a *heteratomic molecule*. Since table salt contains one sodium and one chlorine atom per molecule, or two atoms per molecule altogether, it is also said to be diatomic, just as oxygen.

Hydrogen atoms have a single proton and a single electron. All atoms that have just one proton in their nuclei are atoms of hydrogen. The number of protons in the nucleus of an atom is the key to the identity of the atom. Uranium, for example, appears in various weights, all atoms of uranium containing exactly 92 protons. It is this fact that enables us to call uranium "uranium" and no other name. The number of protons in an atom is called the *atomic number* (abbreviated "Z") of the atom. Since neutral atoms have not lost or gained any electrons, the number of protons equals the number of electrons in orbit around the nucleus of a neutral atom.

In atoms that are more complex than the simple hydrogen atom, *neutrons* exist. A neutron is heavy, like the proton, and also resides in the nucleus of the atom, just as the proton. Unlike the proton, though, it has zero charge. It can, therefore, add to the weight of the nucleus of an atom without affecting the charge of the atom.

One form of the hydrogen atom exists with a neutron, in addition to the proton, in its nucleus. Since the electron is very light, this "heavy hydrogen," or deuterium, weighs almost twice as much as simple hydrogen, which lacks only the neutron. Since both kinds of hydrogen contain only one proton, we are sure that both are hydrogen atoms.

Because of neutrons atoms manifest various weights. Uranium sometimes appears in a form having a weight of 235 amu (*atomic-mass units*) and sometimes in a form having a weight of 238 amu. Both of these forms of uranium have exactly 92 protons in their nuclei. Chemically, these forms are written $_{92}U^{235}$ and $_{92}U^{238}$. The number of neutrons in the nucleus of $_{92}U^{235}$ can be found by subtracting the 92 protons from the total weight 235. There are, therefore, 143 neutrons in an atom of $_{92}U^{235}$. The forms U^{235} and U^{238} are called *isotopes*. They have the same number of protons but different atomic weights. Naturally, they are both isotopes of uranium. Atomic weights are based on the weight of carbon $_6C^{12}$. One amu is 1/12 the weight of a $_6G^{12}$ atom.

The chemical conduct of an element is entirely controlled by the electrons surrounding the nucleus, not by the nucleus itself. Therefore, it stands to reason that the electrons around the nucleus must be arranged in definable groups. The elements, chlorine and fluorine, for example, fall into what is classified as *group VIIA* on the periodic chart of elements. The elements of group VIIA all have atoms that normally tend to gain one electron (per atom) when entering into chemical reactions. Why should all group VIIA elements behave like this?

To arrive at a reasonable answer, the concept of the atom *shell* was developed. The shell of an atom is an area about the nucleus wherein electrons of discrete energy levels are allowed to travel (or orbit). The first shell (called the *K shell*) has the ability to hold 2 electrons and is the closest shell to the nucleus of the atom. The electrons in the atoms, H (hydrogen) and He (helium), are completely enclosed in the K shell. For heavier atoms, which have more than 2 electrons, additional shells (further from the nucleus than the K shell) hold electrons not contained in the K shell (which only holds 2 electrons). Thus, there are additional shells: the L, M, N, O, and P shells. The capacities of these remaining shells are 8, 18, 32, 32, and 10 electrons, respectively, with the P shell furthest from the nucleus of the atom.

To see why chlorine, fluorine, and other group VIIA elements behave with similarity chemically, we must subdivide the electron shells into *subshells*. These are designated with the lower case letters s, p, d, f, and g. Within each shell the capacities for the subshells s, p, d, and f are 2, 6, 10, and 14 electrons, respectively, with the s subshell being the innermost subshell of each shell (the part of the shell closest to the nucleus).

Since the first shell (K shell) can only hold 2 electrons, it can only contain the s subshell. The L shell (which holds 8 electrons) has its own s subshell (which holds 2 electrons) and a p subshell (which holds 6 electrons). For larger shells more subshells are needed. The N shell (which holds 32 electrons) contains s, p, d, and f subshells.

Chlorine, having 17 electrons, has 10 electrons altogether in the first two shells and 7 electrons in the third shell, 5 of which are in the p subshell. The p subshell, which has a capacity of 6 electrons, is incomplete by 1 electron. Since chemical reactions take place in the outermost electron shells and since the outermost shell of chlorine has an incomplete subshell, chlorine tends to enter into reactions that will give it 1 electron per atom. When chlorine enters into such a reaction, in which each chlorine atom gains that one electron, it becomes a chlorine *ion* with a charge of -1 since it has one extra electron.

Fluorine, which has 9 electrons normally, has 2 electrons in the K shell and 7 electrons in the L shell, which is complete with 8 electrons. It too tends to enter chemical reactions in which each atom (of fluorine) gains 1 electron and, in this case, completes the p subshell of the L shell. In this important respect, chlorine, fluorine, and other elements of group VIIA are similar. This concept is very useful when comparing the elements silicon and germanium, which are used in all semi-conductors.

ATOMS IN METALS

Although it was mentioned that when chlorine atoms enter a chemical reaction, they gain one electron per atom, certain chemical reactions leave compounds whose atoms do not lose or gain electrons but instead share them. Consider metals. If the metal atoms are so close together that their outer electron orbits overlap, the attractive force between the atoms is so strong that each atom is fixed in position, and the material formed is a solid. The outer electron encircling its atom has difficulty establishing its orbit from the orbit of the outer electron of the atom adjacent to it, since both orbits overlap; the atoms are that close together. In this case, both atoms share an electron from the orbit of each other. The force existing between these atoms sharing their outer (valence) electrons is known as a *covalent bond.* Since no electrons are given away in this type of reaction, no ions are formed.

Germanium, which has 4 valence electrons, tends to share its outer electrons with other germanium atoms in a *cubic lattice.* A two-dimensional view of this lattice is shown in Fig. 2–1. Each germanium atom is satisfied, as it seems to have 8 electrons in its outer orbit (4 of which are shared). The 4 shared electrons complete the germanium p subshell of the O shell.

In metals not all outer electrons are held in the lattice by covalent bonds. Some electrons have enough energy to free themselves from the bonds and travel throughout the lattice. This freeing of electrons can occur when the atom is heated above Absolute Zero temperature. The addition of heat to the

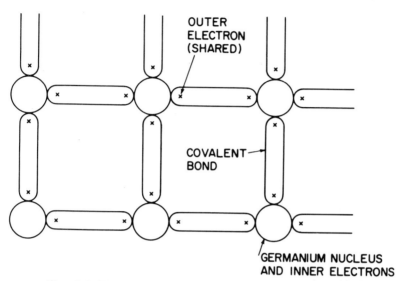

Fig. 2-1. Two-dimensional view of germanium lattice.

electron gives it sufficient energy to escape from the covalent bond, but since it is still under the influence of the electrostatic forces of the atoms close to it as it travels, the electron can not leave the surface of the metal lattice. However, if enough heat is added, the electron can actually leave the surface of the metal. This phenomenon is evident in vacuum tubes in the form of *thermionic emission* from the cathode.

These free electrons which wander throughout the lattice are called *ions* because they are not associated with any particular atom. The atoms whose orbits these free electrons have left are also ions since they have lost 1 electron. The higher the temperature, the more free electrons exist in the metal lattice because of the equivalence of heat and energy.

CONDUCTORS AND INSULATORS

If a battery is hooked up to this metal piece, the electric field set up across the piece causes these free electrons to flow toward the positive terminal of the battery. The electrons then leave the negative terminal of the battery and flow toward the positively charged ions that are left by the free electrons. This electric current exists as long as the free electrons continue to flow. In moving through the lattice, the free electrons encounter some resistance because of their collisions with atoms. If we increase the voltage of the battery, the field across the metal also increases, causing more of the free electrons to flow into and out of the battery (in a given amount of time) than before. This statement is equivalent to *Ohm's law,* written symbolically $I = E/R$. The greater the voltage E across a metal, the greater will be the current flow I through the metal. The greater the resistance R of the metal, the less current will flow. If we heat a metal, for example, there will be more free electrons and positive ions in the metal, causing more collisions with the free electrons trying to reach the positive battery terminal and, thereby, reducing the total current flow.

If a material has all of its outer electrons in covalent bonds, it is a *perfect insulator.* In practice, since there are always some impurities in any material, some free electrons always exist. Good conductors have about 10^{20} the number of free electrons that good insulators have, per given volume.

SEMICONDUCTORS

A semiconductor possesses conductive characteristics to a slight degree but can be made to appear as either a conductor or an insulator. If a semiconductor is heated sufficiently, the atoms receive enough heat to break the covalent bonds between them, thus releasing free electrons for conduction. At lower temperatures a semiconductor behaves as an insulator. Semiconductors without impurities are called *intrinsic semiconductors.* The most useful of these intrinsic semiconductors belong to group IVA of the periodic table (notably, germanium and silicon).

These intrinsic semiconductors do not normally conduct because the outer electrons of all the atoms are in covalent bonds, just as in an insulator. At room temperature, though, the electrons that are bonded weakly have enough heat energy to become free electrons. A much greater amount of heat must be applied to break the covalent bonds of an insulator. The vacancy left by a free electron in a semiconductor acts as a positive charge, or *hole*. A free electron from another atom in the semiconductor may fill the hole, while the atom that the free electron originally left gains a hole. It is this principle which demonstrates how the hole (or vacancy) is free to move throughout the crystal.

Under the influence of an electric field, the holes move (or drift) to the negative plate. Once the hole drifts to the negative plate, a free electron leaves the plate and fills the hole. The fact that these electrons and holes are produced in equal numbers in intrinsic semiconductors limits the usefulness of the semiconductors (by themselves). By introducing impurities into the crystal structure of an intrinsic semiconductor, we can make either the holes or the electrons the main current carrier.

If we introduce into the germanium crystal lattice an atom that has 5 valence electrons (instead of the 4 electrons introduced by all germanium atoms), we get the situation shown in Fig. 2–2. One of the 5 electrons in the "impure" atom is extra, in relation to the lattice. Because all the surrounding germanium atoms have their 4 electrons in covalent bonds, no germanium electrons are free to bond with this extra electron.

Although this extra electron is not normally free (it is still bound to its atom), it often happens that at temperatures near room temperature the electron will gain enough heat energy to break its bond with the parent atom and become a free electron. But notice that the freeing of this electron does not create a hole, unlike the situation in the intrinsic semiconductor. In fact, the overall lattice structure is not even altered by the freeing of

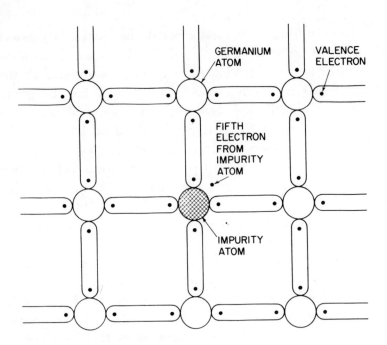

Fig. 2-2. Germanium lattice with "impure" atom (donor).

this electron. The parent atom which just lost this electron is left with 4 electrons; although it is a positive ion (having lost a negative electron), it looks almost like any germanium atom in the crystal. This atom, because it donated a free electron to the crystal, is called a *donor atom*. Typical donor atoms include arsenic, antimony, and phosphorous, all having 5 valence electrons. (These elements belong to group VA of the periodic table.) If many donor atoms are introduced into a semiconductor, the free electrons will appear in large numbers. Electrons, not holes, will be the major carrier of the electric current. Such a material is called an *n-type semiconductor*.

If an atom with 3 valence electrons were added to a germanium intrinsic semiconductor, the opposite situation would exist. In this lattice the crystal would have an extra hole. An electron from a germanium atom might jump into this hole and leave another hole in its place. The atom accepting this electron is called an *acceptor atom*. If many atoms with only 3 valence electrons were added to the germanium lattice, most of the current would be carried by the holes, which would outnumber the electrons. This material would be called a *p-type material*. Acceptor atoms include boron, gallium, and indium (group IIIA of the periodic table).

To review, in an n-type semiconductor, electrons are the major current carriers whereas in a p-type semiconductor, holes are the major current carriers. Normally, at room temperature, all of the impurity atoms of a "doped" semiconductor ionize and create holes or electrons. The germanium (or silicon) atoms of the intrinsic material that was doped outnumber the impurity atoms, normally by a very wide margin. However, raising the temperature of a semiconductor very high causes even the bonds between the germanium electrons to break, resulting in many more holes and electrons. In fact, the ratio of holes to electrons becomes about one to one. Therefore, a doped semiconductor behaves as an intrinsic semiconductor at high temperatures. This explains why there are important temperature limits for semiconductor devices.

THE P-N JUNCTION

When we join n-type and p-type crystals, we get a boundary between the two materials—this boundary is called a *p-n junction*. When this p-n junction is formed, some of the free electrons from the n-type crystal cross the junction to fill the holes in the p-type material. This diffusion takes place in a very short period of time and happens very close to the junction, producing a space-charged region called the *transition region*. (See Fig. 2–3.)

The p-type material actually becomes slightly negative

(because of the additional electrons that crossed the junction), and the n-type material becomes slightly positive (because of the loss of those electrons that crossed the junction from the n-type material). This space-charged region can be represented by an imaginary battery. (See Fig. 2–4.) This space-charged configuration discourages any further electrons from crossing the junction, because electrons near the transition region in the n-type material are repelled by the negative charge in the p-type material just across the junction.

If we were to connect a battery across the p-n junction, the current flowing through the crystal would be dependent on

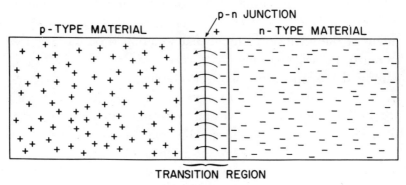

Fig. 2-3. The p-n junction.

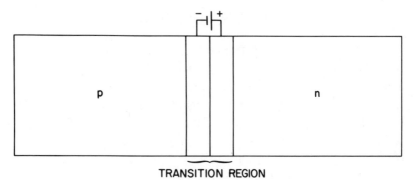

Fig. 2-4. Representation of space-charged region.

the effect of the space-charged region and the polarity of the battery voltage. When the positive terminal of the battery is connected to the p-type material and the negative battery terminal is connected to the n-type material, electrons will be pushed into the junction by the electrons leaving the negative terminal of the battery and will combine with the holes pulled toward the junction from the p-type material. Electrons enter the crystal from the negative battery terminal to replace the electrons that crossed the junction and combine with the holes in the p-type material. In this way current flows. This junction is said to be *forward-biased*. (See Fig. 2–5.)

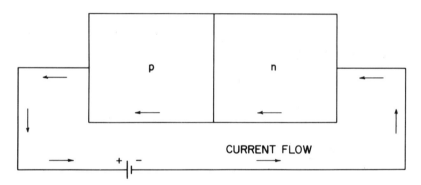

Fig. 2-5. Forward-biasing of p-n junction.

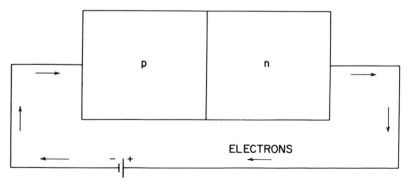

Fig. 2-6. Reverse-biasing of p-n junction.

If the same battery were arranged so that the positive battery terminal were connected to the n-type material and the negative battery terminal were connected to the p-type material, a very different situation would exist. Now the electrons from the n-type crystal are attracted to the positive battery terminal and flow away from the junction. (See Fig. 2–6.) At the same time, electrons from the negative battery terminal fill in the holes of the p-type material. The space-charged region gets wider, and the voltage across the junction rises to equal the battery voltage. The current flow then stops because there is no electric field across either the n or the p regions. In this case the junction is said to be *reverse-biased*.

A typical current-voltage curve for a p-n junction is shown in Fig. 2–7. In the forward-biased region, current rises as voltage rises. Reverse current is usually much lower than forward current.

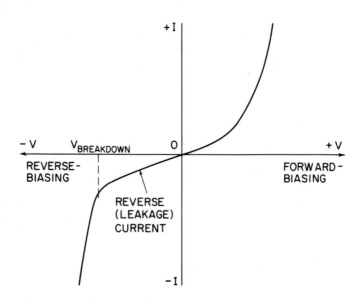

Fig. 2-7. The p-n junction characteristic.

THE DIODE

The semiconductor diode is basically a p-n junction. If we connect a diode in series with a load and join it to a sine-wave oscillator, we obtain rectification. During the portion of the sine wave when the anode of the diode is positive with respect to its cathode, the p-n junction of the diode is forward-biased and current flows from the sine-wave oscillator through the diode and the load and back into the oscillator. The current flowing through the load causes a voltage to appear across it. (See Fig. 2–8.) Some voltage is also dropped across the diode when it is conducting, but it is usually very small (less than 1 V) if a reasonable load resistor is chosen.

In that portion of the sine wave where the anode of the diode is negative with respect to its cathode, the p-n junction of the diode is reverse-biased, almost no current flows, and the voltage across the load resistor is very close to zero. This process is called *half-wave rectification,* shown in Fig. 2–9, since only half of the sine wave of the oscillator appears across the load as an output.

Compared with the process of the vacuum-tube diode, the results of rectification are the same. In the vacuum-tube diode, though, a filament is necessary to raise the temperature of the cathode sufficiently to produce (boil off) electrons. The semiconductor diode, needing no filament, operates at a low temperature, much lower than its vacuum-tube equivalent.

There are many types of semiconductor diodes. The point-contact diode, the oldest semiconductor device, was found in the early crystal receivers. A "cat's whisker" was placed against the crystal surface until the proper point of the crystal was contacted. Point-contact diodes are made better today, but they still must be used in low-power applications. Point-contact diodes are of either germanium or silicon. The silicon type of point-contact diode can be used at higher frequencies than

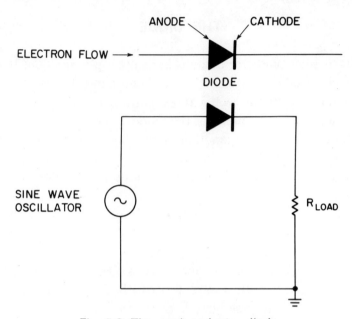

Fig. 2-8. The semiconductor diode.

the germanium type but breaks down if a high reserve voltage is applied across the p-n junction. Its use is restricted to microwave mixers. The point-contact diode has a very small p-n junction.

The point-contact diode junction is formed by a sharp metallic point being brought into contact with a semiconductor material. The semiconductor material is the same type throughout the diode (n-type), and a p-type region forms because the electrons of the n-type material adjacent to the point of contact of the "cat's whisker" and the semiconductor material tend to leave the semiconductor material and enter the metallic "cat's whisker." The lack of electrons at this point in the n-type material constitutes a barrier to conduction of current through the junction, which is overcome only when a battery of the correct polarity is applied across the junction. This supplies a voltage of sufficient magnitude to cause electrons to flow

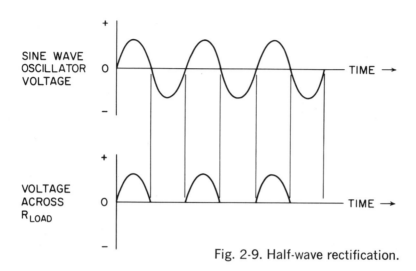

Fig. 2-9. Half-wave rectification.

into the p-type region from the semiconductor. When the junction is reverse-biased, the barrier is increased, and the electrons in the p-type material continue to flow away from the junction. Point-contact diodes have also been constructed of p-type material, with conduction being formed by hole current.

The more common diodes have much wider junctions and are, therefore, more useful. These diodes are manufactured by different processes, depending upon how the junction is made.

Along with the p-n junction is an inherent capacitance. All semiconductor diodes have some junction capacitance, which appears in parallel with the diode. At high frequencies when the junction of the semiconductor diode is reverse-biased, even though the diode has a very high back resistance, radio-frequency current can still flow through this capacitance. This places a frequency limitation on the use of the diode as, for example, a high-frequency detector. Because point-contact diodes have a small junction, their capacitance is a fraction of a picofarad (pF). For modern "grown junction" diodes, though, the junction capacitance can be 1–50 pF. This is why point-contact diodes can be used at very high frequencies, whereas "grown," "alloy," or "diffused" junction diodes (three processes for making typical diodes) cannot. Because grown, alloy, and diffused diodes have larger junction areas, they can be used at much larger power levels than point-contact diodes.

The junction capacitance of a diode is usually a disadvantage. However, in the varactor diode, this capacitance is used to advantage. In the varactor diode, the capacitance of the diode junction increases as the reverse-biased voltage (across the diode) decreases. A graph of a typical varactor diode is shown in Fig. 2–10. The varactor diode is often used in place of the reactance tube in frequency-control circuits. Compared with the reactance tube, the varactor gives a greater capacitance change for identical differences in applied diode bias. The varactor diode does not require the filament and plate power supplies that a reactance tube needs. Varactor diodes are used in parametric amplifiers for radar systems, because of their high frequency capabilities.

It was mentioned above that germanium and silicon are each used as an intrinsic material in semiconductors. The differences between these two elements can best be illustrated by a diagram showing the characteristics of a junction using germanium and of one using silicon. (See Fig. 2–11.) This diagram clarifies several important points. For a given forward bias, more current is drawn by the germanium diode than by the silicon diode. At normal states of diode conduction, a 0.3-V drop appears across the germanium diode, whereas a 0.6-V drop appears across the silicon diode if both are utilized in a circuit drawing, for example, 1 mA (milliampere).

Until the reverse-voltage breakdown (across the diode) is reached, the leakage current through a silicon diode will be much lower than that current through the germanium diode at the same voltage. In an ideal diode, the leakage current should be zero, when the diode is reverse-biased.

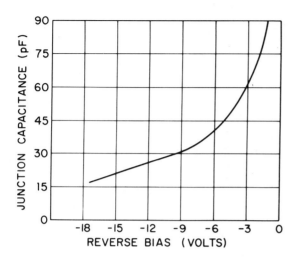

Fig. 2-10. Junction capacitance (pF) vs. reverse bias (volts).

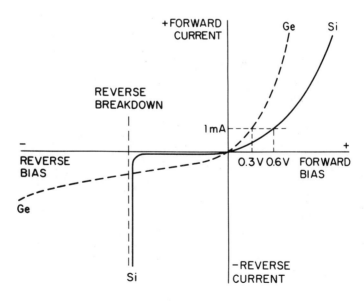

Fig. 2-11. Germanium and silicon characteristics.

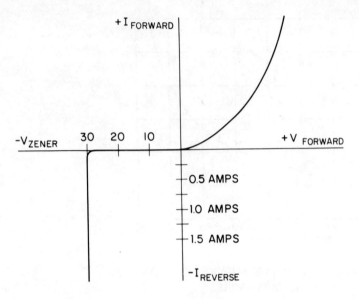

Fig. 2-12. Zener diode characteristic.

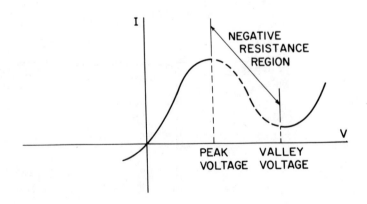

Fig. 2-13. Tunnel diode characteristic.

It is clear that the reverse-voltage breakdown is quite severe for a silicon diode, although it is not quite so well defined for germanium diode junctions. The reverse-voltage breakdown characteristic of a silicon diode leads into a special class of diodes called *silicon-zener diodes.* These diodes are normally reverse-biased into the proper region of operation. In the proper region of operation of the diode, the diode maintains a constant voltage independent of load current within a wide range.

A typical zener-diode characteristic is shown in Fig. 2–12. Referring to the figure, for any load drawing between 5 mA and 1.25 A (amperes), the voltage across the diode is 30 V and is independent of load. When used in this "control region," the zener diode is very useful in power supplies formerly requiring VR tubes (voltage-regulator tubes).

In the VR tube, a certain voltage must be reached to start ionization of the gas. After this ionization has taken place, the voltage across the tube drops and remains at a constant level. For zener-diode regulator, the supply voltage must only exceed the zener voltage by a few volts. A VR tube can only regulate voltages down to about 70 V. Zener diodes, on the other hand, can regulate down to about 2 V. Gas-tube regulators, on the other hand, have some initial voltage drift when the regulator is first turned on, and stabilization of the regulator voltage may take several minutes. Zener diodes show little, if any, drift of regulating level.

Tunnel Diodes

The tunnel diode is a semiconductor which, by virtue of a high degree of doping, has unique characteristics. This high degree of doping causes the Fermi levels (energy states) of the holes in the p-type material and the electrons in the n-type material to overlap. This means that the electrons in the n-

type material and the holes in the p-type material are in prox-
imity in terms of energy and that the electrons have only to
cross the junction barrier (about 10^{-6} cm, centimeters) to cause
conduction. According to classical atomic theory, however, a
particle must have an energy magnitude at least equal to the
height of the potential barrier to traverse the barrier. For barriers as thin as those estimated in the tunnel diode, quantum
mechanics dictates that there is a large probability that an
electron will penetrate through (not over) the barrier. This
behavior is referred to as tunneling and is responsible for radio-
active emissions.

As a consequence of tunneling electrons, the characteristic
for the tunnel diode, shown in Fig. 2–13, is obtained. The negative resistance region of Fig. 2–13 is that part of the characteristic between the peak and the valley of the characteristic.
This makes the tunnel diode useful in circuits such as oscillators and multivibrators where an "active" device is normally
needed. (Active devices include transistors, triodes, tetrodes,
and so forth.)

The negative resistance feature of the tunnel diode characteristic can be explained as follows. At the peak of the characteristic, a large number of electrons have tunneled across
the barrier, as the holes in the p-type material have received
enough energy (from the biasing battery) to cause the required
overlapping energy bands. As the voltage is increased, though,
conduction decreases rapidly because the two energy bands
move apart. At this point of the valley, tunneling stops (the
probability of an electron crossing the barrier and transcending
the energy-level difference, which is now large, approaches
zero), and normal diode-conduction action takes place.

The negative resistance region of the characteristic makes
it possible for the tunnel diode to amplify. This region is similar in shape to the negative portion of the plate characteristic
of the vacuum-tube tetrode.

Silicon-Controlled Rectifiers

The silicon-controlled rectifier (SCR) is a semiconductor "switch" whose operation is similar to that of the thyratron vacuum tube. The main advantages of the SCR are its low response time (about 1 μs, microsecond) and its ability to handle high power (some can handle a kilowatt). The representation for an SCR, along with its characteristics, is shown in Fig. 2–14.

With reverse bias the diode behaves as any normal diode. With forward bias current is blocked until the breakdown voltage $V_B K$ is reached. (The breakdown voltage is nondestructive to the SCR.) When the breakdown voltage is reached, the resistance of the SCR drops quickly to a low level.

When the SCR is positively biased below the breakdown voltage, the diode can be switched to its conducting state by applying some gate-to-cathode current. To switch the SCR off, the cathode current must be reduced to a value less than the holding current I_H. This can be accomplished by dropping the anode voltage to zero or by making it negative with respect to the cathode.

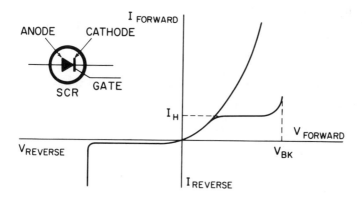

Fig. 2-14. SCR characteristic.

TABLES: Much in the diode tables (Tables 2–1, 2–2, 2–3, and 2–4) is self-explanatory. Some explanation will be given to aid the reader in interpreting the tables as well as to demonstrate some facts about diodes, which are covered in the text.

In Table 2–1 under the column "Forward Voltage V_F @ Indicated Fwd, Current," we see listed the various voltage drops (in volts) across the indicated diodes, when the diode is conducting the indicated current. The important point here is that at different values of current being conducted by the diode, the voltage drop across the diode varies. This fact has been demonstrated in Fig. 2–11 where, for the hypothetical diodes chosen, it was shown that at 1 mA current conduction, the voltage drop across the germanium diode was 0.3 V and the voltage drop across the silicon diode was 0.6 V. From the characteristic we saw that as the diode was conducting less current, there was less of a voltage drop across it. Likewise, as the diode was conducting more current, there was more of a voltage drop across it. This is why it is important to indicate the forward current at which the voltage drop across the diode is measured.

The column, "Reverse Current @ Indicated Voltage," is divided to show the effect of the reverse current as the temperature of the diode is changed. This reverse (or leakage) current rises as the diode temperature increases. The leakage current is also a function of the diode bias (reverse bias), which is why it is important to indicate the voltage at which the leakage current is measured.

The column, "Min. SAT. Voltage or Min. Breakdown Voltage V @ Indicated Reverse Current," is self-explanatory. The breakdown voltage is not always destructive to the diode, but without further manufacturer's information, it is best to limit the reverse voltage on the diode to within the value listed in this column.

Since the junction capacitance of a diode is dependent on the voltage impressed across the diode junction, the capacitance listed under the column heading, "Total Capacitance @ Indicated Voltage," indicates the junction bias at which it was measured. The capacitance gives an indication of the frequency limit of the device.

"Power Dissipation" and "Forward Current Steady-State DC" are absolute maximum ratings for the diode, which, if exceeded, void the guarantee of the diode.

In Table 2–2, because the junction is germanium and not silicon, various items are different. First, because the germanium breakdown is not as severe as the silicon-diode breakdown, the PRV (peak reverse voltage) is generally higher than that of its silicon counterpart. Since the PRV is really the maximum value of reverse bias for the germanium diode, the column, "Max. Cont. Reverse Voltage," indicates a safer limit for diode reverse bias.

The "Maximum Forward Current" column is broken up according to the input waveform. In general, the shorter the peak of the input waveform, the greater the peak that the diode can withstand. This is true because of the heating effects of the waveform, which influence the stability of the diode junction. Thus, the diode can withstand a greater maximum forward current on a surge than on an average.

In Table 2–4, the important points of the tunnel-diode characteristics are listed. The "Peak Point Current" and the "Valley Point Current" have been explored above. These values are different for different diodes as is the case with the "Peak Voltage." The tunnel diode "Capacitance" and "Max. Series Resist. Rs" are useful to designers of tunnel diode oscillator and amplifier circuits. The column, "Typical Resistive Cut-off Frequency," demonstrates the extremely high frequencies at which tunnel diodes can be used.

TABLE 2-1.
SILICON DIODES
Signal Diodes—Planar Epitaxial

Type	Forward Voltage V_F @ Indicated Fwd. Current Volts	MAXIMUM Reverse Current @ Indicated Voltage I_R				Min. Breakdown Voltage V @ Indicated Reverse Current or Min. SAT. Voltage Volts	Total Capacitance @ Indicated Voltage pf	MAXIMUM		Comments
		25°C μa	100°C μa	125°C μa	150°C μa			Power Dissipation @ 25°C. mW	Forward Current Steady State DC mA	
1N251	1.0, 5 ma	0.2,-10V 20.0,-20V	10.0,-10V	—	—	40	—	150	—	
1N252	1.0, 10 ma	0.1,-5V 20.0,-12V	—	10.0,-5V	—	30	—	150	—	
1N625	1.0, 4 ma	1,-20V	30.0,-20V	—	—	30	—	200	20	
1N626	1.0, 4 ma	1,-35V	30.0,-35V	—	—	50	—	200	20	
1N659	1.0, 6 ma	5,-50V	25.0,-50V	—	—	50	2.7,-10V	250	100	
1N659A	1.0, 10 ma	0.025,-50V	—	—	5.0,-50V	75	2.7,-10V	250	100	
1N789	1.0, 10 ma	1,-20V	30,-20V	—	—	30	—	500	180	
1N790	1.0, 10 ma	5,-20V	30,-20V	—	—	30	—	500	180	
1N791	1.0, 50 ma	5,-20V	30,-20V	—	—	30	—	500	250	

1N793	1.0, 10 ma	1,-50V	30,-50V	—	—	60	—	500	180	
1N794	1.0, 10 ma	5,-50V	30,-50V	—	—	60	—	500	180	
1N795	1.0, 50 ma	5,-50V	30,-50V	—	—	60	—	500	250	
1N811	1.0, 1 ma	1.0,-10V 20.0,-15V	—	10.0,-10V	—	30	—	150	40	
1N812	1.0, 2 ma	0.1,-10V 20.0,-20V	—	10.0,-10V	—	40	—	150	60	
1N813	1.0, 5 ma	0.5,-5V 20.0,-10V	—	10.0,-5V	—	20	—	150	75	
1N814	1.0, 2 ma	0.1,-20V 20.0,-30V	—	10.0,-20V	—	50	—	150	60	
1N3068	1.0, 5 ma	0.1,-20V	—	—	100,-20V	30, 5μa	6.0,-0V	250	—	
1N3124	1.0, 20 ma	0.1,-40V	10.0,-40V	—	—	40	2.0,-6V	125	50	
1N3206	1.0, 10 ma	0.025,-20V 5.0,-80V	—	—	50,-20V	100	4.0,-0V	150	—	
1N3600 1N4150	1.0,200ma(cc)	0.1,-50V	—	—	100,-50V	50	2.5,-0V	500	—	
1N3604 1N4151	1.0, 50 ma	0.05,-50V	—	—	50,-50V	75, 5μa	2.0,-0V	250 500	115	Very high speed, high conductance, computer diode. Subminiature package.
1N3605 1N4152 1N4533	See Table 1	0.05,-30V	—	—	50,-30V	40, 5μa	2.0,-0V	250 500 500	115	Controlled conductance, very high speed diode. Subminiature package.

TABLE 2-1 (cont'd).
SILICON DIODES
Signal Diodes—Planar Epitaxial

Type	Forward Voltage V_F @ Indicated Fwd, Current Volts	MAXIMUM Reverse Current @ Indicated Voltage I_R				Min. SAT. Voltage or Min. Breakdown Voltage V @ Indicated Reverse Current Volts	Total Capacitance @ Indicated Voltage pf	MAXIMUM Power Dissipation @ 25°C. mW	Forward Current Steady State DC mA	Comments
		25°C μa	100°C μa	125°C μa	150°C μa					
1N3606 1N4153 1N4534	See Table 1	0.05,-50V	—	—	50,-50V	75, 5μa	0.0,-0V	250 500 500	115	
1N3607	1.0, 50 ma	0.05,-50V	—	—	50,-50V	75, 5μa	2.0,-0V	150	115	Very high speed, high conductance diode in micro-miniature package.
1N3608	See Table 1	0.05,-30V	—	—	50,-30V	40, 5μa	2.0,-0V	150	115	
1N3609	See Table 1	0.05,-50V	—	—	50,-50V	75, 5μa	2.0,-0V	150	115	Controlled conductance, very very high speed diode in micro-miniature package.

	0.85,20ma(cc)	0.1,-50V	—	—	40,-50V	50	4.0,-0V	250	200	Very high speed, electrically identical to the Polaris G-321 high reliability diode.
1N3873 1N3873/HR										
1N4069 1N4154 1N4536	1.0, 30 ma	0.1,-25V	—	—	100,-25V	35, 5μa	4.0,-0V	250 500 500	115	Economy type.

TABLE 2-1 (cont'd).

	TABLE 1			TABLE 2		TABLE 3		TABLE 4	
I_F	V_F		I_F	V_F		V_F		V_F	
mA	Min. mV	Max. mV	mA	Min. mV	Max. mV	Min. mV	Max. mV	Min. mV	Max. mV
0.1	0.490	0.550	0.01	0.74	1.09	1.19	1.54	0.430	0.550
0.25	0.530	0.590	0.1	0.97	1.22	1.52	1.77	0.510	0.630
1.0	0.590	0.670	1.0	1.21	1.41	1.85	2.05	0.600	0.710
2.0	0.620	0.700	10.0	1.38	1.58	2.12	2.32	0.690	0.800
10.0	0.700	0.810	100.0	1.54	1.84	2.36	2.66	0.800	0.920
20.0	0.740	0.880	—	—	—	—	—		

TABLE 2-2.
GERMANIUM DIODES
Signal Diodes—Point-Contact

Type No.	PRV	Max. Cont. Reverse Voltage	Maximum Forward Current — ma				Maximum Reverse Current				Comments
			Average	Recurrent Peak	1 sec. Surge		Volts	μa	Volts	μa	
1N34	75	60	50	150	500		−10	50	−50	800	General purpose
1N34A	75	60	50	150	500		−10	30	−50	500	
1N35	75	60	50	150	500		−10	10			Matched pair of 1N34A
1N38	120	100	50	150	500		−3	6	−100	500	
1N38A	120	100	50	150	500		−3	6	−100	500	High reverse voltage
1N38B	100		50	150	500		−3	6	−100	500	
1N48	85	70	40	150	400		−50	833			
1N51	50	40	20	100	300		−50	1660			
1N52	85	70	40	150	400		−50	150			
1N52A		50	40	150	400		−50	100			General purpose detector
1N54	50	35	40	150	500		−10	10			
1N54A	75	50	40	150	500		−10	7	−50	60	
1N58	120	100	40	150	500		−100	600			
1N58A	120	100	40	150	500		−100	600			High reverse voltage
1N63	125	100	40	150	400		−50	50			

Type										Description
1N65	85	70	40	150	400	−50	200	50	50	General purpose
1N67	100	80	35	100	500	−5	5	−50	50	
1N67A	100	80	30	100	300	−5	5	−50	50	
1N68A	130	100	30	100	500	−100	625	−50		High reverse voltage
1N69	75	60	40	125	400	−10	50	−50	850	
1N69A	75	60	40	125	400	−10	30	−50	500	
1N70	125	100	30	90	350	−10	25	−50	300	General purpose
1N70A	125	100	30	90	350	−10	25	−50	300	
1N75	125	100	40	150	400	−50	50			
1N118A	75	60	70	250	400		20	−50	100	
1N273	35	30	80		450	−20				High conductance
1N279	39	30	80		450	−20	200			
1N281	75	60	75		400	−10	30	−50	500	
1N292	75	60	70		150			−50	200	
1N298A	85	70	30		300	−5	10	−40	250	Computer diode
1N309	40	30	100			−20	100			High conductance
1N313		100	40		500	−20	10	−100	50	Low leakage diode
1N449	40	30	60			−10	10	−30	30	High conductance
1N497	30	20	60			−20	20			Low leakage
1N774	70	60	50		450	−10	15	−50	150	High conductance
1N776	30	20	45		400	−10	200	−30	500	
1N777	70	60	50		450	−10	25	−50	125	Switching diode

TABLE 2-3.
Video Detector Diodes*

Type No.	Maximum Reverse Current			Max. Average Rectified Forward Current mA
	PRV	Volts	μa	
1N60	30	−10	67	50
1N60A	40	−10	60	50
1N60C	50	−10	67	50
1N64	25	−10	100	50
1N87A	30	−1.5	30	50
1N295A	40	−10	200	35
1N616	30	−10	100	50

TABLE 2-4.
Tunnel Diodes

Type	MAXIMUM			Peak Voltage V_P mV	Max. Series Resist. R_S Ohms	Typical Resistive Cut-off Frequency f_{ro} KMC
	Peak Point Current I_P mA	Valley Point Current I_V mA	Capacitance C pF			
1N2939	1.0 ± 10%	0.14	15	65 Typ.	4.0	2.2
1N2939A	1.0 ± 2.5%	0.14	10	60 ± 10	4.0	2.6

1N2940	1.0 ± 10%	0.22	10	65 Typ.	4.0	2.2
1N2940A	1.0 ± 2.5%	0.22	7	65 ± 10	4.0	2.6
1N2941	4.7 ± 10%	1.04	50	65 Typ.	2.0	2.6
1N2941A	4.7 ± 2.5%	1.04	30	65 ± 10	2.0	3.9
1N2969	2.2 ± 10%	0.48	25	65 Typ.	3.0	2.5
1N2969A	2.2 ± 2.5%	0.48	15	65 ± 10	3.0	3.3
1N3149	10.0 ± 10%	2.2	90	65 Typ.	1.5	2.6
1N3149A	10.0 ± 2.5%	2.2	50	65 ± 10	1.5	3.1
1N3150	22.0 ± 10%	4.8	150	65 Typ.	1.0	2.2
1N3712	1.0 ± 10%	0.18	10	65 Typ.	4.0	2.3
1N3713	1.0 ± 2.5%	0.14	5	65 ± 7	4.0	3.2
1N3714	2.2 ± 10%	0.48	25	65 Typ.	3.0	2.2
1N3715	2.2 ± 2.5%	0.31	10	65 ± 7	3.0	3.0
1N3716	4.7 ± 10%	1.04	50	65 Typ.	2.0	1.8
1N3717	4.7 ± 2.5%	0.60	25	65 ± 7	2.0	3.4
1N3718	10.0 ± 10%	2.20	90	65 Typ.	1.5	1.6
1N3719	10.0 ± 2.5%	1.40	50	65 ± 7	1.5	2.8
1N3720	22.0 ± 10%	4.80	150	65 Typ.	1.0	1.6
1N3721	22.0 ± 2.5%	3.10	100	65 ± 7	1.0	2.6

USES OF DIODES

The electronics industry has only barely scratched the surface of the many uses to which semiconductor devices can be put. Even today, new and varied applications are being found for semiconductors, and completely new concepts in equipment design are being developed in order to take better advantage of the best qualities of semiconductors.

The diode is the basic semiconductor device and, often, the most commonly used in electronic equipment. The manner in which the diode is constructed dictates to a great degree where it can best be employed. Now that you have learned about diodes with respect to their construction and theory, we will discuss some of the uses of the diode, describing how they function in typical circuits. In explaining the following circuits, we will provide a theoretical discussion of how the diode performs. Theory will be dealt with only for the purpose of understanding the operation of the diode. In a later chapter, we will again look at these circuits with an eye to servicing them. There are many hundreds of diodes, each one different from the next as is the case with circuits. If you understand the basic circuit, then you should be able to grasp the function of the diode in any variation of the basic circuit. Here, then, are typical basic circuits in use today.

The AM Detector

The AM detector, illustrated in Fig. 2–15, is a basic circuit of the type of detector used in AM receivers, portable radios, and various pieces of communications equipment.

Theory of operation. The importance of the low forward resistance of a diode is demonstrated in this circuit. The detector diode allows the negative-voltage envelope of each cycle to be an input to capacitor C. Capacitor C charges to the voltage peak of each cycle, and the voltage across it varies with the amplitude variations of the RF signal, which are, in turn, con-

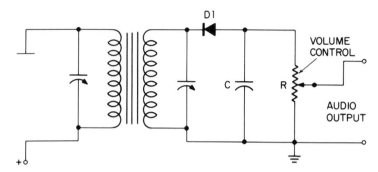

Fig. 2-15. AM detector.

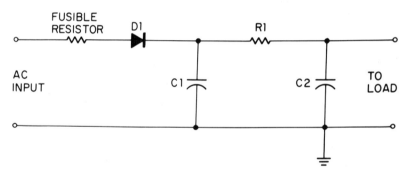

Fig. 2-16. Half-wave power rectifier.

trolled by the amplitude variations of the input signal. In this way, the RF signal is "demodulated," and since only the negative-voltage envelope of each cycle is applied to capacitor C, the signal is demodulated by a rectification process. Potentiometer R, called the *volume control*, is used to vary or control the amount of audio output to the next stage.

The diode could be placed in the circuit backwards, in regard to its polarity, and the circuit would still function properly. The next stage, though, would receive the opposite polarity input.

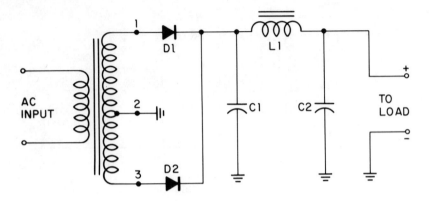

Fig. 2-17. Full-wave power rectifier.

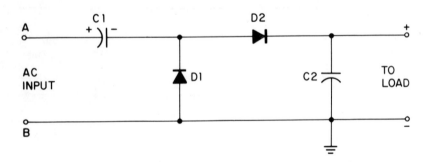

Fig. 2-18. Voltage doubler, power rectifier, half-wave.

The Half-wave Power Rectifier

The half-wave power rectifier is used in ac/dc-type radios, TV sets, and other types of communications equipment. Figure 2–16 shows a typical power supply in use today. It can only be used where power requirements are not too large, because the heavy power drain affects both filtering quality and voltage output.

Theory of operation. The diode allows the positive portion of the ac cycle to pass current into the load resistor, and since a sine wave is only positive for 50 per cent of each ac cycle, the diode passes current into the load for only 50 per cent of the cycle. The diode then converts the ac to a pulsating dc. Capacitor C1 charges up to the peak voltage of the ac during each cycle and then discharges through R1. The components R1 and C2 act to smooth out these pulsations, and by the time the dc reaches the load, it is comparatively pure. The fusible resistor is used as a current-limiting device to protect the diode. It also acts as a fuse should a short develop.

The Full-wave Power Rectifier

The full-wave power rectifier is the most commonly used rectifier. Most manufacturers of communications equipment use this kind of rectifier because its output is essentially ripple-free when properly filtered. The full-wave rectifier has been used in computers, communications equipment, test instruments, TV sets, and high-fidelity equipment. The power transformer, shown in Fig. 2–17, has a center-tapped secondary winding. The transformer is also used to change the voltage to the required value from that of the line voltage.

Theory of operation. When the voltage across the transformer primary winding makes terminal 1 more positive than terminal 2, diode D1 conducts, charging up capacitor C1. On the second half of the ac cycle, terminal 3 is more positive than terminal 2; diode D2 conducts and C1 receives another pulse of dc voltage. It can be seen that, for each reversal of input voltage, either D1 or D2 conducts, thus providing two pulses of voltage to C1 during each cycle. This means that although the input frequency may be only 60 Hz (hertz), actually C1 is being pulsed at twice that rate, making the pulsating dc voltage easier to filter. The full-wave power rectifier has excellent voltage regulation, high efficiency, and the capacity to handle large power requirements.

The Voltage Doubler, Power Rectifier, Half-wave

Figure 2–18 illustrates an economical type of voltage-doubler, which is used in some TV sets, radios, and phonographs.

Theory of operation. When the ac input is such that point B is more positive than point A, diode D1 will conduct, causing capacitor C1 to charge up to the peak applied voltage. During the second half of the ac cycle, point A is positive with respect to point B, and the line voltage plus the voltage across C1 is applied to diode D2. Since the voltage across C1 is the same as the line voltage, twice the line voltage is applied to D2. When D2 conducts, the dc output voltage charges up capacitor C2. This means that the voltage that is applied to the load is also twice the line voltage. Since both D1 and D2 are half-wave rectifiers, the regulation and efficiency for this type of rectifier approximates that of the half-wave rectifier.

The Voltage Doubler, Power Rectifier, Full-wave

The full-wave voltage-doubler (see Fig. 2–19) offsets the disadvantages of the half-wave voltage-doubler. The efficiency and regulation of the full-wave doubler are not as good as those of the full-wave, non-doubling rectifier.

Theory of operation. When the ac input is such that point A is positive with respect to point B, diode D1 conducts and charges up capacitor C1 to the peak value of the line voltage. On the next half of the cycle, point B becomes positive with respect to point A, causing diode D2 to conduct. When D2 conducts, C2 is charged up to the peak value of the line voltage. Since C1 and C2 are in series across the load, the voltages across C1 and C2 are added to obtain the load voltage.

The Bridge Rectifier

The bridge rectifier (see Fig. 2–20) is another efficient type of rectifier utilizing four diodes.

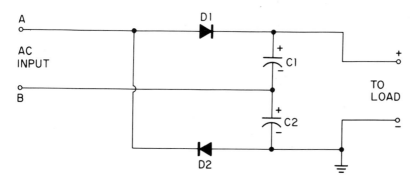

Fig. 2-19. Voltage doubler, power rectifier, full-wave.

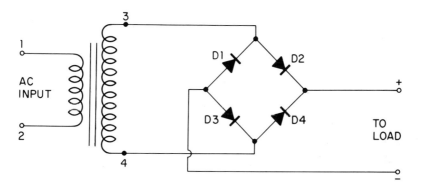

Fig. 2-20. Bridge rectifier.

Theory of operation. When the ac input causes point 3 to be positive with respect to point 4, diodes D2 and D3 will conduct. Since these diodes are wired across the load, voltage is delivered to the load. During the next half-cycle, the voltage across points A and B is reversed causing diodes D4 and D1 to conduct, which allows voltage to appear across the load

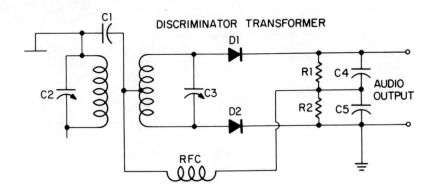

Fig. 2-21a. Foster-Seeley discriminator.

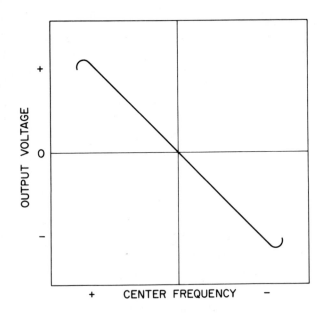

Fig. 2-21b. Output waveform of discriminator circuit.

since these diodes are also connected across the load. Since this rectifier operates during both halves of the ac input cycle, it is a full-wave rectifier. The bridge rectifier has a very low ripple output, excellent voltage regulation, and high efficiency.

The Foster-Seeley Discriminator, FM Detector

The Foster-Seeley discriminator (see Fig. 2–21a) is widely used in FM receivers and TV sets. In this discriminator detection is caused by the phase and frequency shifting of the input signal. Because the discriminator is highly susceptible to amplitude variations (static, ignition noise, and so forth), a noise-limiter stage must precede it.

Theory of operation. A voltage induced in the secondary winding is 90° out of phase with the primary current. The primary voltage is also introduced into the secondary winding through capacitor C1 and combines with the voltages in each half of the secondary winding. Because of this, the voltage on one-half of the secondary winding leads the primary voltage and the other half lags the primary voltage at center frequency.

These equal and opposite polarity voltages are applied to the diodes D1, which is wired across R1, and D2, which is wired across R2. Both R1 and R2 are in series, and since two voltages are present, both equal and of opposite polarity, the result will be zero output voltage.

When the incoming signal deviates from the resonant frequency, the 90° phase relationship between the primary and the secondary voltages changes, thereby causing an unequal voltage to be applied to the diodes. A dc voltage proportional to the difference between the RF voltages applied to the diodes will be present across the series load resistors. This means that when the input signal varies in frequency across the resonant frequency of the discriminator, an audio voltage proportional to the frequency deviation, representing the original modulation, will appear in its output, as Fig. 2–21b shows.

The Ratio Detector, FM Detector

The ratio detector (see Fig. 2–22) is another type of FM detector used in FM radios, TV sets, and other signal-processing equipment. The advantage of the ratio detector is that it is not susceptible to amplitude variations, so a limiter stage is not needed. This circuit is almost identical to the Foster-Seeley discriminator, except in the way the diodes are wired in respect to their polarity, and the manner in which the audio is removed or extracted from the RF signal.

Theory of operation. In this circuit both diodes are wired in series through R1 and are wired across the secondary of T1. The two diodes are wired up in this way so that both of them will conduct on the same half-cycle of the RF. This causes a voltage to develop across R1, with the plate of D2 being the negative side. The very large capacity of the C3 causes the voltage to remain constant, which serves the purpose of eliminating any amplitude variations (noise, pulse, and so forth) so that this type of detector does not need a limiter stage preceding it.

The rectified voltage across C1 is proportional to the voltage across D1, and that across C2 is proportional to the voltage across D2. Since the voltages across the diodes will vary because of the changes in the instantaneous frequency of the incoming signal, the voltages that appear across C1 and C2 will also be proportionately different. The voltage across C1 will be the larger voltage for frequencies below the center frequency and will be a smaller voltage for frequencies above the center frequency.

The voltages across C1 and C2 are additive and are kept constant by the large capacity of C3. The net result is that although the ratio of the voltages varies at an audio rate, their total remains constant. The voltage across C1 varies at an audio rate when an FM signal is present. The audio output is taken from R2, which is considered a volume control. The negative

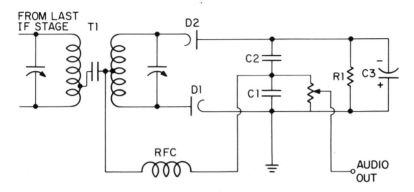

Fig. 2-22. The ratio detector.

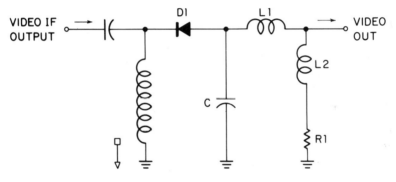

Fig. 2-23. Video detector.

voltage developed across C3 can be used for any automatic gain control circuit; in FM receivers it would be used to control the IF (intermediate-frequency) stages.

The Video Detector

Figure 2–23 illustrates the basic circuit of a video detector

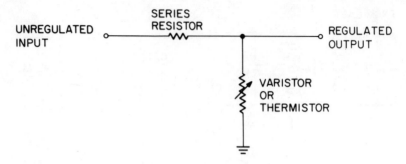

Fig. 2-24. Voltage regulator.

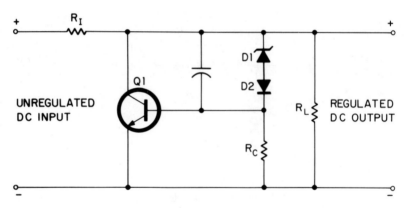

Fig. 2-25. Semiconductor voltage regulator.

used in TV sets as well as radar receivers. This video detector works in exactly the same manner as the low-voltage rectifier, except that the video detector is used over a greater frequency range. The frequencies that the video detector must handle lie between 30 Hz and 4.5 MHz (megahertz). Because of the broad band of frequencies that the video detector must demodulate, series and parallel peaking coils are used in order to provide a linear output. When used in a TV set, the video detector is also used to demodulate the sound as well as synchronizing signals.

Voltage Regulators

Figure 2–24 illustrates a basic voltage regulator circuit, using either a varistor or a thermistor. This means of regulating is commonly used in computers, test equipment, and communications equipment.

Theory of operation. When the varistor is used, it operates in the following manner. An increase in the unregulated source voltage causes the internal resistance of the varistor to decrease, loading down the circuit and resulting in a larger voltage drop across the series resistor. This prevents the output voltage from rising. When the thermistor is used, being a temperature-sensitive device, it reacts to a change in its internal temperature. When the input voltage rises, this causes more current to flow through it, which raises its temperature, and in turn, lowers its internal resistance. This has the same effect on the series resistor, again tending to keep the output voltage constant. The thermistor, being a temperature-sensitive device, is not very fast in reacting to changes of voltage and, as such, is used only where slow variations of voltage are present. One of the big disadvantages of thermistors is the fact that they are affected by external ambient temperatures.

The Semiconductor Voltage Regulator

The regulator circuit, shown in Fig. 2–25, is used in conjunction with others and is fast acting and unaffected by its surrounding temperature. It too is used in computers, communications equipment, and test equipment. The zener diode has a characteristic curve that tends to keep the voltage across it constant for rather large current changes. This has the effect of regulating the output voltage. Refer to the voltage-regulator theory covered in Chapter III for theory of operation.

The Counter Circuit, Positive

Figure 2–26 illustrates a typical counter circuit used in computers and test instruments. Counters are used in computers to control the sequence of events and are utilized in test instruments as frequency-determining elements.

Theory of operation. Positive pulses applied to the input of capacitor C1 make the cathode of D2 negative with respect to ground. D2 conducts through R1, charging up C1 during pulse time. At the end of the pulse, the voltage across C1 causes D1 to conduct, which in turn discharges C1. The voltage drop across R1 can be used to control a succeeding stage. To make this into a negative counter, diodes D1 and D2 should be reversed. This counter circuit can be used to produce a dc output that is proportional to the pulse-repetition rate or a series of pulses whose pulse rate is proportional to that of the input.

The AND Gate

The AND gate (see Fig. 2–27) is used in computer-logic circuits.

Theory of operation. If the input to D1 is at a low level—ground, for example—then D1 is forward-biased causing its anode to be at ground potential. The output then is at ground potential. If the input to D2 is high (positive), D2 is reverse-biased so that it will not conduct current. If the input to D1 is low and if the input to D2 is high or low, the output voltage will be zero. The same situation exists for D2. If the input to D2 is low, the output will be low whether the input to D1 is high or low. If the inputs to diodes D1 and D2 are both high, however, the output will also be high. This is because both diodes will be reverse-biased, and the output voltage will be V_{cc} R2/(R1 + R2), which provides some positive voltage.

Because the output is positive only if both D1 and D2 have true inputs (positive inputs in this example), this gate is called

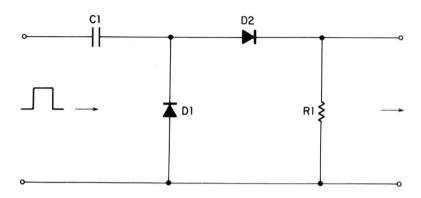

Fig. 2-26. Counter circuit, positive.

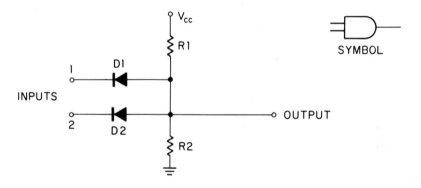

Fig. 2-27. The AND gate.

an *AND gate*. This circuit is also used with pulse inputs. If an input pulse is applied to one diode, no output pulse will result until another pulse is applied to the input of the other diode simultaneously. Sometimes one of the inputs is a timing pulse so that the output pulse occurs only at designated times. The output pulse can be used to control or trigger other circuits.

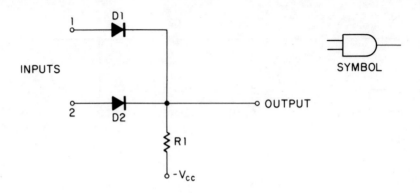

Fig. 2-28. The OR gate.

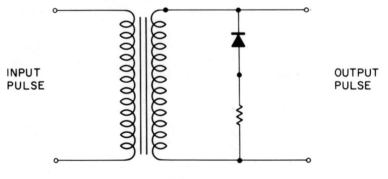

Fig. 2-29. Damping circuit.

The OR Gate

The OR gate (see Fig. 2–28) is used in computer-logic circuits, oscilloscopes, and other timing and communications-type circuits.

Theory of operation. If the input to D1 is at ground (low) and the input to D2 is at ground, then diodes D1 and D2 are conducting and the output voltage is zero. Now, let us say that we change the input of D2 to 20 V (high). Since D2 is forward-biased, it conducts, and its anode assumes a voltage of 20 V. Since the voltage input to D1 is still zero, D1 is now reverse-biased. Since the cathode of D2 is connected to the output, the output reaches a level of 20 V when the input to D2 is at 20 V. With the same logic, we can demonstrate that if the input to D1 were 20 V and the input voltage to D2 were zero, the output would be at a 20-V level. Now, let us assume that both inputs are at 20 V; then both diodes will be conducting, and the output will again be 20 V.

Since the output is high when either or both inputs are high, this gate is called an *OR gate*. Notice again that if both inputs are low, the output is low (or false). If this circuit is used with pulse inputs, an output pulse appears if either input is high.

The Damping (Anti-ringing) Circuit

The damping circuit (see Fig. 2–29) is used mainly in TV sets. The ringing occurs when pulses having sharp rise and fall time characteristics go through an inductance or a transformer. This occurs when the sweep voltage across the horizontal deflection coils collapses suddenly, during retrace. This ringing would appear across the face of the picture tube unless damped out.

Theory of operation. The diode is wired in such a way as to develop the pulse across its high back resistance. The high resistance of the diode does not load down the winding, and the positive pulse is passed on to the output. When the pulse is suddenly removed from the primary of the transformer, the magnetic field built up around the winding collapses and the circuit "rings." As this occurs, the voltage across the winding reverses, and the low forward resistance of the diode acts as a short circuit. When this happens, the resistor acts in series with the coil to damp out any tendency to ring. The value of the resistor determines the amount of damping. In some cases, overdamping is deliberately done to preclude the possibility of false pulses getting through to the output. Too much damping will, of course, stop any pulse from reaching the output.

The Clamp, Limiter

Clamps and limiters are used in receivers, computers, and various other pieces of electronic equipment. The clamp circuits, shown in Fig. 2–30, are used to limit the size of a pulse. The way the diode is wired in the circuit and the polarity of the biasing voltage as well as the kind of biasing voltage (ac, dc) determine to a great extent how the circuit works.

Theory of operation. The upper clamp limits the maximum positive-voltage output. If V_{bias} were connected to ground, for example, then no matter what voltage input were applied, the maximum voltage at the output would be at zero because the diode would be conducting at a positive voltage. If V_{bias} were connected to +3 V, the maximum output voltage would be +3 V, because any applied voltage greater than +3 V would cause the diode to conduct, which would make the anode of the diode and, therefore, the output voltage +3 V.

The lower clamp operates in a similar manner, with the exception that V_{bias} is negative. Let us assume to start with that V_{bias} for the lower clamp is ground. Then the output voltage cannot become more negative than ground, because for a negative voltage at the diode cathode, the diode conducts and causes its cathode voltage to be about the same as its anode voltage, or zero. If V_{bias} were some negative voltage, −3 V for example, then the output voltage could not become any more negative than −3 V, using the same reasoning.

The resistors used in the upper and lower clamps limit the current passing through the diode in its conducting state.

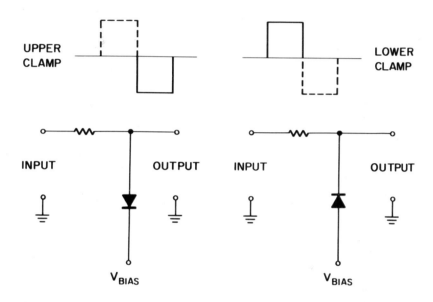

Fig. 2-30. Upper and lower clamps.

CHAPTER III

Transistors

The development of the transistor has led to an amazing reduction in the size of most electronic equipment. The simplest transistor can be formed by placing a second p-n junction next to the first in such a way that both p regions (or n regions) are common (see Fig. 3–1). This is called a *junction transistor.* To achieve gain from the device, we must forward-bias one p-n junction and reverse-bias the other p-n junction. The electric field developed across this junction causes the attraction by the righthand junction of the electrons injected into the p region from the forward-biased lefthand junction. The electrons in the p region are minority carriers (holes are the majority carriers in p regions), and the righthand junction, because it collects these minority carriers, is called the *collector.* The lefthand junction is called the *emitter,* and the region between the emitter and collector is called the *base.* The transistor depicted in Fig. 3–1 is an *npn-junction transistor,* because the p-type material is shared by the two p-n junctions, and there are two distinct regions of n-type material.

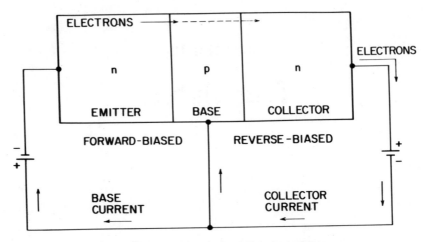

Fig. 3-1. Biased npn-junction transistor.

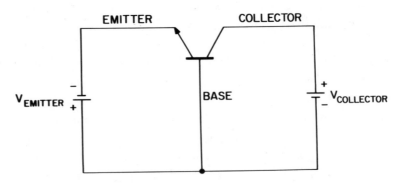

Fig. 3-2. Biased npn-junction transistor.

The reverse-biased righthand junction causes holes to be generated in the collector region because of the electrons leaving the collector to the positive side of the battery. The majority of the electrons injected into the base from the left-hand junction diffuse through the base-collector junction and combine with the holes in the collector. The factor that de-termines how many electrons will diffuse into the base region and collector region is the magnitude of the reverse bias (col-lector-to-base bias). Actually, some "pairing" of electrons and holes takes place in the lefthand area of the p-n junction, but with sufficient reverse bias, the pairing accounts for only a very small percentage of the current. The pairing current is emitter-to-base current, commonly called *base current*. A schematic representation of Fig. 3–1 is given in Fig. 3–2.

A transistor can also be formed by taking two p-n junctions and joining them so that the n regions are common (see Fig. 3–3). This is called a *pnp transistor*, since there are two dis-tinct p regions and only one (common) n region. In this case, the electric field developed across the junction causes electrons to leave the n material (base) and enter the lefthand p material (emitter). We might also say, with at least equal validity, that the holes in the emitter region (holes are the majority current carriers in p-type materials) are attracted to the electrons in the n region. Some of these holes combine with the electrons to form the base current. If the reverse bias is of sufficient mag-nitude, the holes travel through the base and into the collector (righthand p material). Once the holes enter the collector region, they are attracted to the negative terminal of the bat-tery, and they then combine with the electrons from the bat-tery. This electron-hole current is what constitutes the collec-tor current of the transistor. In the pnp transistor, the collector current is opposite in direction to the direction of hole move-ment (majority carrier movement). This is because current is really electron flow (by convention), and electrons always move in a direction opposite to the direction that holes move. Similarly, the base current in a pnp transistor is opposite in direction to the direction of hole movement (majority current carrier movement). Because electrons are the majority carriers in npn transistors, the majority current carrier movement and current direction are the same. Figure 3–4 is a schematic diagram of a biased pnp transistor. Notice the change in the direction of the arrow on the emitter lead from the direction it has in Fig. 3–2 (npn transistor). This arrow is what distinguishes the pnp transistor from the npn transistor symbolically.

TRANSISTOR PARAMETERS

The majority current carriers that reach the collector in pnp and npn transistors are always somewhat less than the amount of those carriers that left the emitters of these transistors. This is another way of saying that the collector current is less than the emitter current (in vacuum tubes, the plate current is always at least slightly less than the cathode current, by analogy). The forward current gain of a transistor is the ratio of collector current to emitter current and is given the Greek symbol *alpha* (α or a.) This parameter is usually about 0.95 in a good transistor, and its value depends on how efficiently the emitter generates carriers into the base. Its efficiency is dependent on the magnitude of the emitter current. Its value also depends on how wide the base region is, since the wider the base, the fewer the carriers that reach the collector. Those carriers that do not reach the collector form the base current. Since alpha is a dc measurement ($\alpha = I_c/I_e$), it tells us little about how the transistor operates with a varying signal input. This will be discussed later.

Another important parameter is given the Greek symbol *beta* (β). If the emitter current is I_e and the collector current is αI_e, the base current must be $I_e - \alpha I_e$ or $I_b = (1 - \alpha)I_e$. This

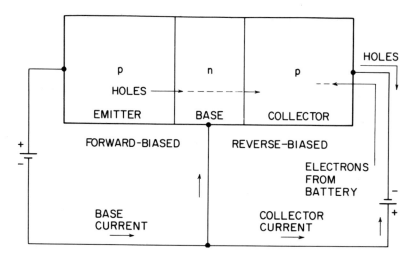

Fig. 3-3. Biased pnp-junction transistor.

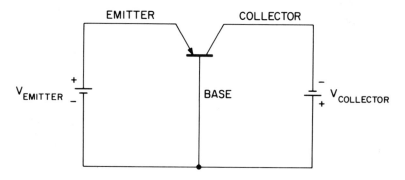

Fig. 3-4. Biased pnp-junction transistor.

is true because $I_e = I_c + I_b$. If we take the ratio of collector current to base current, we get $I_c/I_b = \alpha/(1-\alpha) = \beta$. If alpha is 0.99, for example, beta equals $0.99/(1-0.99) = 99$. Transistors may have betas of several hundred, and a beta of 100 is a typical beta value for many types of transistors.

We can apply these parameters to the three basic transistor circuits: common-base (see Fig. 3–5), common-emitter (see Fig. 3–6), and common-collector (see Fig. 3–7). In the common-base circuit, the current gain is the ratio of output current to input current, or gain $= I_c/I_e = \alpha$. In the common-emitter circuit, the gain is the ratio of output current to input current, or gain $= I_c/I_b = \beta$. For the common-collector circuit, the signal input is applied to the base, and the signal output is taken from the emitter. The gain is, therefore, the ratio of $I_e/I_b = 1/(1 - \alpha)$. If $\alpha = 0.99$, which is a reasonable alpha, then $\beta = \alpha/(1-\alpha) = 99$ and $1/(1-\alpha) = 1/0.01 = 100$. We can see that while the common-emitter and common-collector circuit configurations have a high gain, the common-base circuit configuration has a current gain that is less than one.

We can draw other comparisons between these three circuit configurations also. Since a forward-biased diode (p-n junction) has relatively low resistance, and since the emitter-base junction of a transistor is forward-biased (for conduction), we know that the emitter-base junction resistance is relatively low. Since a reverse-biased diode has a relatively high resistance, and since the collector-base junction is reverse-biased, we know that the collector-base junction resistance of a transistor is relatively high. Inasmuch as the exact values for these resistances depend greatly on the transistor, terminations, and circuit configurations, no simple generalizations can be made as to the exact resistance values. We can, however, present a typical comparison, as it is of some value in deciding which circuit configuration to use to do a specific job.

Table 3–1 is a table of characteristics versus circuit con-

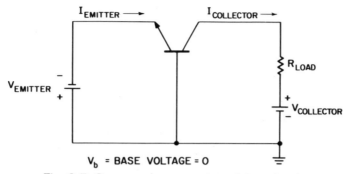

Fig. 3-5. Common-base npn transistor circuit.

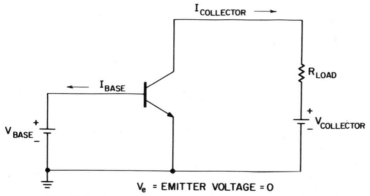

Fig. 3-6. Common-emitter npn transistor circuit.

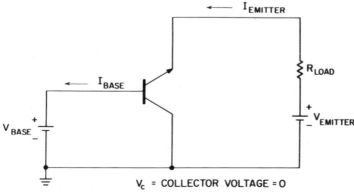

Fig. 3-7. Common-collector npn transistor circuit.

figuration for a sample transistor. Table 3–1 indicates that the common-collector circuit has the highest input impedance, the common-base circuit has the highest output impedance, and the common-emitter circuit has the highest power gain. In addition, the common-emitter circuit is the only circuit having input-output phase inversion. The common-base, common-emitter, and common-collector circuits behave similarly to the grounded-grid, common-cathode, and cathode-follower, vacuum-tube circuits, respectively. Collector-current/collector-voltage characteristics for the common-base and common-emitter circuits are given in Figs. 3–8 and 3–9. Since the collector voltage is zero for the common-collector circuit, no characteristic is given.

TABLE 3-1.

Characteristics	Common Base	Common Emitter	Common Collector
Input Impedance	50 Ω	850 Ω	250 kΩ
Output Impedance	1 MΩ	50 kΩ	200 Ω
Current Gain	< 1	90	92
Voltage Gain	2	2	< 1
Power Gain	Low	High	Medium

h Parameters

Hybrid parameters (h parameters) are a common set of parameters used to describe the behavior of a transistor under small-signal conditions. The h parameters provide an easy means for describing or measuring the performance of a transistor at low or high frequencies. When applied to a transistor (h parameters are used for "black boxes" too), the h parameters are the following:

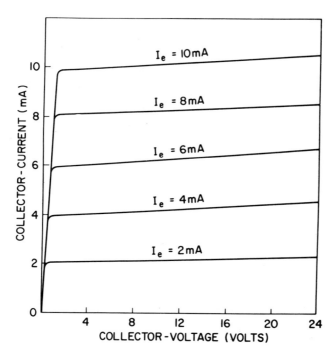

Fig. 3-8. Common-base collector-current/collector-voltage characteristic.

h_{ib} = common-base input impedance
h_{fb} = common-base forward current transfer ratio
h_{rb} = common-base reverse voltage transfer ratio
h_{ob} = common-base output admittance (1/output impedance)

For common-collector and common-emitter circuits, the second subscript becomes c and e respectively (*i.e.*, the common-collector h parameters are h_{ic}, h_{fc}, h_{rc}, and h_{oc}; the common-emitter h parameters are h_{ie}, h_{fe}, h_{re}, and h_{oe}). The derivation of the h parameters is beyond the scope of this book, although their use when supplied by the transistor manufacturer will be covered toward the end of this chapter. Where lowercase subscripts are used in the h parameters, a ratio of incremental

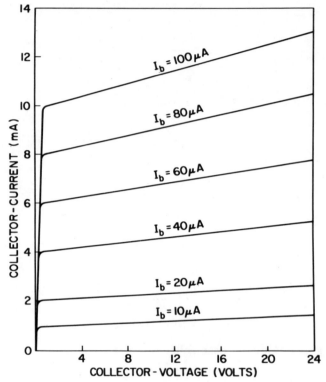

Fig. 3-9. Common-emitter collector-current/collector-voltage characteristic.

changes is indicated. For example, h_{fb} is approximately equal to the ratio of the incremental change in the collector current to the incremental change in the emitter current that caused it. Where uppercase subscripts are used, a direct ratio is indicated $h_{FB} = I_c/I_e$. The following approximates can be made*:

$$\text{common-base input impedance:} \quad h_{ib} \cong \frac{\Delta V_e}{\Delta I_e}\bigg|V_c$$

$$\text{common-emitter input impedance:} \quad h_{ie} \cong \frac{\Delta V_b}{\Delta I_b}\bigg|V_c$$

*$\big|V_c$ means the measurement is made holding the collector voltage constant.

$$\text{alpha: } h_{fb} \cong \frac{\Delta I_c}{\Delta I_e} \left(\text{also,} \quad h_{FB} = \frac{I_c}{I_e} \right)$$

$$\text{beta: } h_{fe} \cong \frac{\Delta I_c}{\Delta I_b} \left(\text{also,} \quad h_{FE} = \frac{I_c}{I_b} \right)$$

common-base output admittance: $h_{ob} \cong \frac{\Delta I_c}{\Delta V_c} \bigg|_{I_e}$

common-emitter output admittance: $h_{oe} \cong \frac{\Delta I_c}{\Delta V_c} \bigg|_{I_b}$

common-base voltage feedback ratio: $h_{rb} \cong \frac{\Delta V_e}{\Delta V_c} \bigg|_{I_e}$

common-emitter voltage feedback ratio: $h_{re} \cong \frac{\Delta V_b}{\Delta V_c} \bigg|_{I_b}$

Figures 3-10 through 3-14 were drawn using h parameter transistor analysis. These figures demonstrate some very important transistor characteristics, and typical values have been inserted to give the reader a general knowledge of transistors. Input resistance, output resistance, current gain, voltage gain, and power gain versus load resistance are illustrated in these figures.

ADDITIONAL TRANSISTOR CHARACTERISTICS

I_{CBO}

If a transistor were perfect, when we opened the emitter circuit, no collector current would flow. In practice, however, some collector current does flow in this case. This current, designated I_{CBO}, is both temperature and voltage-dependent and can be a great portion of the base current in low-level applications; in large-signal applications, it can cause thermal runaway. Figure 3–15 illustrates I_{CBO} versus junction temperature, and Fig. 3–16 illustrates I_{CBO} versus collector-to-base voltage.

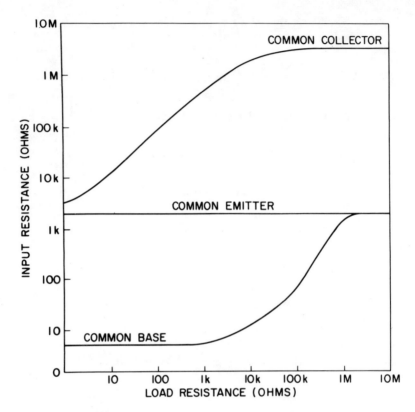

Fig. 3-10. Input resistance vs. load resistance.

Junction Capacitances

When the transistor is used above audio frequencies, various reactances of the transistor come into play. Because of the strong electric field across the regions separating the base from the collector and emitter, various "barrier" capacitances exist. These junction capacitances C_C and C_E separate the collector and base, and emitter and base, respectively. In a physical model for the transistor, we would see that these capacitances do not actually tie directly to the base but instead go to the transistor internal base-resistance model r_b which then goes to the base.

The sum of junction capacitances C_E and C_C is equal to the sum of transistor transition capacitance C_T and transistor diffusion capacitance C_D. The transition capacitance is a voltage-dependent capacitance due to the electric field across the transistor base-emitter and base-collector barriers. The diffusion capacitance is a current-dependent capacitance due to current flowing through these barrier regions. Since the collector is reverse-biased, it has very little diffusion capacitance (there is very little current flow) and C_C is, therefore, made up primarily of transition capacitance. The emitter junction capacitance C_E is composed primarily of the diffusion capacitance, since the emitter is forward-biased (there is a great deal of current flow).

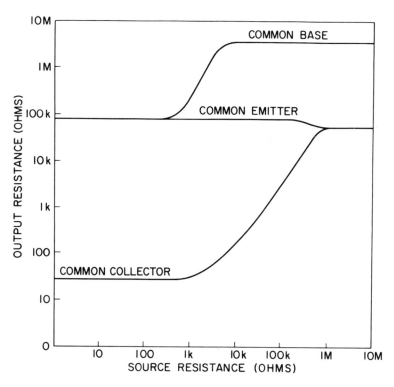

Fig. 3-11. Output resistance vs. source resistance.

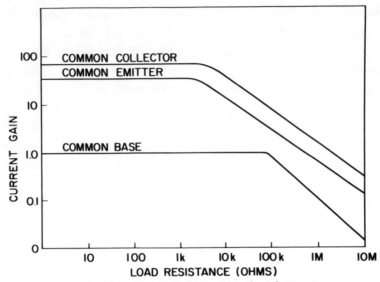

Fig. 3-12. Current gain vs. load resistance.

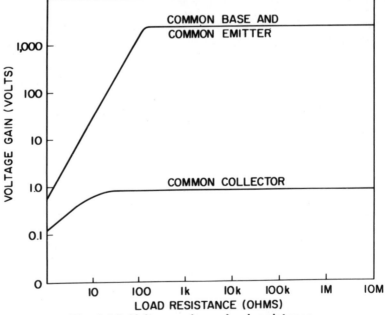

Fig. 3-13. Voltage gain vs. load resistance.

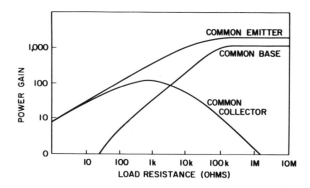

Fig. 3-14. Power gain vs. load resistance.

Transistor Resistances

Transistors have internal resistances in addition to capacitances which are exhibited at high frequencies. One resistance is the resistance between a point in the active region of the transistor base and the point on the external transistor-base contact. Because the base spreads out from the center of the junction to the outside of the transistor in alloy junction transistors, this resistance is called the *base spreading resistance.* Similar resistances are associated with bringing the active collector and emitter regions to the external transistor leads.

Lead Inductances

The lead inductances for a transistor are quite small and are important only at VHF (very high frequency) and above where they are large enough to act as radio-frequency chokes. Vacuum tubes also have a lead inductance problem at high frequencies. Usually, however, the lead inductance in vacuum tubes becomes a problem at lower frequencies than transistor lead inductance, because longer leads are necessary to bring out the active region of the vacuum tube to the tube pins than are necessary to bring out the active region of a transistor to the external transistor contacts.

High-Frequency Operation

Obviously, transistor high-frequency operation is dependent upon all the capacitances and resistances of transistor characteristics. Manufacturers of transistors are constantly working to improve the packaging of transistors in order to keep the associated capacitance and resistance parameters low.

A measure of the frequency limitation of the transistor is the gain-bandwidth product (f_t). As can be expected, f_t is dependent upon the parameters of the transistor and is given by the equation $f_t = \dfrac{1}{2\pi[T_B + R_e(C_E + C_C)]}$ where T_B equals base-transition time, and R_e is the emitter resistor. Figure 3–17 is an illustration of gain versus frequency for a typical high-frequency transistor.

COMPARISON OF TRANSISTORS TO VACUUM TUBES

We have already pointed out that the common-base, common-collector, and common-emitter transistor circuits resemble, functionally, the grounded-grid, cathode-follower, and common-cathode, vacuum-tube circuits, respectively. We can also say that a similar relationship exists between the base, collector, and emitter of a transistor and the grid, plate, and cathode of a triode.

The transistor is essentially a current-controlled device, because differences in input current affect the output of the transistor. The vacuum tube is a voltage-controlled device, because differences in voltages between the vacuum-tube input elements (grid and cathode, for example) control the output. Whereas the common-base current amplification factor α is a ratio of the change in collector current caused by a change in emitter current, the vacuum-tube, voltage-amplification factor μ is the ratio of change in plate voltage to the change in grid voltage that produced it.

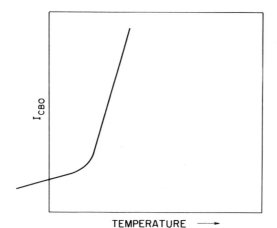

Fig. 3-15. Leakage current (I_{CBO}) vs. junction
temperature.

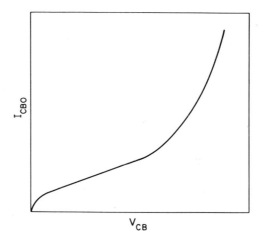

Fig. 3-16. Leakage current (I_{CBO}) vs. collector-
to-base voltage (V_{CB}).

The electrons in vacuum tubes flow through the grid before reaching the plate, whereas in a transistor the current carriers flow through the base before reaching the collector. In general, vacuum tubes are high-voltage, low-current devices, whereas transistors are high-current, low-voltage devices. Input and output impedances for transistor and vacuum-tube circuits with

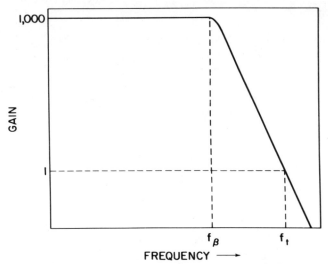

Fig. 3-17. Gain vs. frequency response for high-frequency transistor.

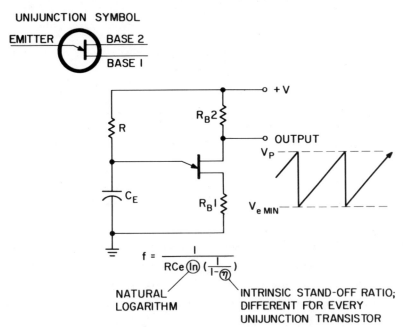

UNIJUNCTION SYMBOL

Fig. 3-18. Unijunction relaxation oscillator circuit.

similar configurations are similar in magnitude. Power ratings and heat capabilities of vacuum tubes are far greater than those of transistors. Frequency limitations for transistors are, as in vacuum tubes, limited by the state of the art in manufacturing.

SPECIAL TRANSISTOR TYPES

Unijunction Transistors

The unijunction transistor is quite different from a normal transistor because its characteristics put it in almost a different component family. A unijunction transistor has a trigger voltage V_P, a low firing current I_P, a negative-resistance characteristic, and a high pulse current capability. This makes the unijuction transistor very useful in voltage-current sensing and comparator circuits, timing and oscillator circuits, and trigger circuits.

The "peak point" characteristic for a unijunction is very important since it determines triggering voltage in bistable circuits, frequency of unijunction oscillators, and threshold level in comparator circuits. Temperature affects unijunctions in such a way as to cause frequency deviations in unijunction-oscillator circuits. A typical unijunction sawtooth (relaxation) oscillator is shown in Fig. 3–18.

Field-Effect Transistors

A field-effect transistor (FET) is a semiconductor current path whose resistance is controlled by the application of an electric field perpendicular to the current. This electric field is a result of the reverse-biasing of a p-n junction. The three elements of the field-effect transistor are the "gate," "source," and "drain." The FET behavior is closer to the pentode vacuum tube than the triode tube, even though the FET has only three elements. Field-effect transistors are most useful at low levels of signal where their high-input impedance and very low noise level make them useful as high-frequency input amplifiers.

TABLES: Sample transistor tables (Tables 3–2 and 3–3) are provided in the following pages. Transistor maximum ratings are given in the tables along with some transistor electrical parameters. Definitions of column headings are given below.

P_C mW: Collector dissipation in milliwatts. If this dissipation is exceeded, the transistor may be destroyed as the dissipation primarily is expended in heating up the junction. Overheating of the transistor collector-base junction usually causes serious accompanying detrimental effects to the transistor.

BV_{CE}, BV_{CB}*:   Breakdown voltage in common-emitter configuration CE or common-base configuration CB*. Although the breakdown of the transistor is not always destructive breakdown (i.e., momentary exceeding of this value may not destroy the transistor), prolonged operation at or above this collector voltage will almost certainly ruin the transistor.

I_C mA: Maximum collector current in milliamperes.

T_J °C;   Maximum allowable junction temperature. If this value is exceeded, thermal runaway may be caused, resulting in a high-leakage current and associated ill effects on performance.

MIN. h_{fe}-h_{FE}* @ I_C mA: The small-signal current gain h_{fe} or direct current gain h_{FE}* at a particular level of collector current (in milliamperes). This value of current gain is a function of collector current and as such can be expected to vary as the collector current is varied. Since this is a minimum value, the gain may be higher than shown in this column. This is because transistor manufacturing techniques cannot control the current gain to a very accurate extent.

MAX. $I_{CO}(\mu A)$ @ V_{CB}:   Maximum leakage current (in microamperes) at a particular collector-to-base bias voltage. I_{CO} is also a function of transistor temperature. As a rule, silicon transistors have a lower I_{CO} than germanium transistors.

TABLE 3-2.

JEDEC No.	Type	Use	Maximum Ratings				Electrical Parameters			
			P_C mW @ 25°C	BV_{CE} BV_{CB}*	I_C mA	T_J °C	MIN. h_{fe}-h_{FE}*	@ I_C mA	MAX. I_{CO} (μa)	@ V_{CB}
2N2016	NPN	Pwr	150W	65	10A	200	15*	5A	200	40
2N2017	NPN	AF	5W	60	1A	200	35/20*	10/1A	10	30
2N2020	NPN	Pwr	40W	150*	2A	175S	25*	100	100	100
2N2021	NPN	Pwr	40W	200*	2A	175S	25*	100	100	100
2N2022	PNP		150	15*	50	100J	35		3.0	
2N2032	NPN	Pwr	85W	45	5A	200S	20*	2A	20ma	45
2N2033	NPN	Pwr		60	3A	200	20*	500	150	80
2N2034	NPN	Pwr		60	3A	200	20*	1A	150	80
2N2035	NPN	Pwr		60	3A	200	20*	1.5A	150	80
2N2036	NPN	Pwr		60	3A	200	20*	2A	150	80
2N2038	NPN	AF		45	500	200S	12*	200	15	30
2N2039	NPN	AF		75	500	200S	12*	200	15	30
2N2040	NPN	AF		45	500	200S	30*	200	15	30
2N2041	NPN	AF		75	500	200S	30*	200	15	30
2N2042	PNP		200	105*	500		50	200		
2N2042A	PNP		200	105*	200	100	50		25	
2N2043	PNP		200	105*			113			
2N2043A	PNP		200	105*	200	100	113		25	
2N2048	PNP	Sw	150	15	100	100S	50*	10	5	5
2N2048A	PNP	Sw	150	20	100	100S	50*	10	3	15
2N2049	NPN-PL		800	75*		200J	60*		.01	
2N2059	PNP	Sw	60	10*	50	100S	20*	.10	5	5
2N2060	NPN-PL	Diff	500	100*		200J	35*	.01	.002	80
2N2061	PNP	Sw		10	3A	85S	10*	500	2ma	20

TABLE 3-2 (cont'd).

JEDEC No.	Type	Use	Maximum Ratings				Electrical Parameters			
			Pc mW @ 25°C	BVCE BVCB*	IC mA	TJ°C	MIN. hfe·hFE*	@ IC mA	MAX. ICO (μa)	@ VCB
2N2062	PNP	Sw		10	3A	85S	20*	2A	2ma	20
2N2063	PNP	Sw		15	3A	95S	10*	2A	400	2
2N2064	PNP	Sw		15	3A	95S	20*	2A	400	2
2N2065	PNP	Sw		25	3A	95S	10*	2A	400	8
2N2066	PNP	Sw		25	3A	95S	20*	2A	400	2
2N2067	PNP	AF		25	3A	95S	20*	500	3ma	40
2N2068	PNP	AF		55	3A	95S	20*	500	3ma	80
2N2069	PNP	AF		40*	12A	95S	30*	5A	15ma	40
2N2070	PNP	AF		80*	12A	95S	30*	5A	15ma	80
2N2071	PNP	AF		40*	12A	95S	30*	5A	15ma	40
2N2072	PNP	AF		80*	12A	95S	30*	5A	15ma	80
2N2074	PNPN	Sw	200	50	1.0A	150S				
2N2083	PNP	MF	100	30*	10	85S	25*	1	12	12
2N2084	PNP	IIF	125	20	10	100S	40	1	8	6
2N2085	NPN		150	33*	500	100	100		5.0	
2N2086	NPN		600	120*	500	300S	70*		2.0	
2N2087	NPN		600	120*	500	300S	65*		2.0	
2N2101	NPN	Pwr		40	3A	200S	15*	1A	30	30

TABLE 3-3.

JEDEC No.	Type	Use	Maximum Ratings				Electrical Parameters			
			P_C mW @ 25°C	BV_{CE} BV_{CB}*	I_C mA	T_J°C	MIN. h_{fe}·h_{FE}*	@ I_C mA	MAX. I_{CO} (μa)	@ V_{CB}
2N2381	PNP	Sw	300	15	500	100S	40*	200	7	5
2N2382	PNP	Sw	300	20	500	100S	40*	200	7	5
2N2383	NPN		85WC	60	5A	200S	20*	1.5A	1ma	80
2N2384	NPN	AF	85WC	60	5A	200S	20*	1.5A	1ma	80
2N2387	NPN	AF	300	45	30	175J	60	1	.010	45
2N2388	NPN		300	45	30	175J	150	1	.010	45
2N2389	NPN	AF	450	75*	500	200J	30	1	.010	60
2N2390	NPN	AF	450	75*	500	200J	50	1	.010	60
2N2391	PNP	AF	300	20	50	175J	15	10	10	25
2N2392	PNP	AF	300	20	50	175J	30	10	10	25
2N2393	PNP	AF	450	35	300	175J	15	1	1	30
2N2394	PNP	AF	450	35	300	175J	25	1	1	30
2N2395	NPN	AF	450	40	300	200J	20*	150	.010	30
2N2396	NPN	AF	450	40	300	200J	40*	150	.010	30
2N2397	NPN	Sw	300	15	200	200J	25*	10	.1	15
2N2398	PNP	VHF	60	20*	50	100J	10*	2	10	10
2N2399	PNP	VHF MXR	60	20*	50	100J	10*	2	10	10
2N2400	PNP	Sw	150	7	100	100S	30*	10	3	5
2N2401	PNP	Sw	150	10	100	100S	50*	10	1.5	5
2N2402	PNP	Sw	150	12	100	100S	60*	10	1.5	5
2N2403	NPN	Sw	1W	60	1A	200S	20*	600	1	30
2N2404	NPN	Sw	1W	60	1A	200S	40*	600	1	30
2N2405	NPN		1W	90	1A	200S	60*	150	.010	100
2N2410	NPN	Sw	800	30	800	200J	30*	150	.3	30

TABLE 3-3 (cont'd).

JEDEC No.	Type	Use	Maximum Ratings				Electrical Parameters			
			P_C mW @ 25°C	BV_{CE} BV_{CB}*	I_C mA	T_J °C	MIN. h_{fe}-h_{FE}*	@ I_C mA	MAX. I_{CO} (µa)	@ V_{CB}
2N2411	PNP	Sw	300	20	100	200J	20*	10	.010	25
2N2412	PNP	Sw	300	20	100	200J	40*	10	.010	25
2N2413	NPN	IF	300	18	200	300S	30*	10	.1	20
2N2414	NPN	Diff	600	28	500	200J	50	5	.025	60
2N2415	PNP	IF	75	10	20	100J	15	2	5	10
2N2416	PNP	IF	75	10	20	100J	10	2	5	10
2N2417		Si Uni								
2N2418		Si Uni								
2N2419		Si Uni								
2N2420	PNP	Si Uni Pwr Sw	90WC	100*	5A	100S	20*	2A	5ma	100
2N2423	PNP	Sw	375	40*	50	160S	30*	5	0.1	30
2N2424										
2N2425	PNP	Sw	375	30*	50	160S	25*	5	0.1	30
2N2426	NPN	Lo PA	150	40*	200	100S	35*	1	20	40
2N2427	NPN	IF/RF	500C	40	50	200S	20*	.010	0.5	40
2N2428	PNP	Lo Pwr	500	32*	100	75S	50*	2	10	10
2N2429	PNP	Lo Pwr	500	32*	100	75S	65*	2	10	10
2N2430	NPN	Lo Pwr	280	32*	300	75S	60*	100	10	10
2N2431	PNP	Lo PO	550	10*	1A	90S	60*	300	10	10
2N2432	NPN	Ch	300	30	100	175	50*	1	0.01	25
2N2433	NPN	Sw	800	45	1A	200	30	1	.001	60
2N2434	NPN	Sw	800	45	1A	200	50	1	.001	60
2N2435	NPN	Sw	800	80	500	200	30	1	.001	90
2N2436	NPN	Sw	800	80	500	200	50	1	.001	90
2N2437	NPN	Ampl	800	75	500	200	18	1	.001	75
2N2438	NPN	Ampl	800	75	500	200	36	1	.001	75
2N2439	NPN	Ampl	800	75	500	200	76	1	.001	75

Type		Use								
2N2440	NPN	Sw	800	80	500	200	50	1	.001	90
2N2443	NPN	A Pwr	4W	100		200S	30	1	.0015	90
2N2444	PNP	Ampl	85WC	80	10A	110S	50	0.5A	20ma	80
2N2445	PNP	Ampl	90WC	50	15A	100S	30	0.5A	20ma	100
2N2446	PNP	Sw	90WC	60	7A	125S	15*	5A	0.5ma	30
2N2447	PNP	AF	75	24	100	85S	25	1	10	20
2N2448	PNP	AF	75	24	100	85S	25	1	10	20
2N2449	PNP	AF	75	20	100	85S	50	1	10	20
2N2450	PNP	AF	75	20	100	85S	50	1	10	20
2N2451	PNP	Sw	200	5	50	85S	25*	10	5	6
2N2453	NPN	Diff	200	30	50	200	150*	1	.005	50
2N2453A	NPN	Diff	200	50	50	200	150*	1	.005	60
2N2454	PNPN	SCR, Sw								
2N2455	PNP	Sw	150	8	200	100S	40*	30	2	6
2N2456	PNP	Sw	150	8	200	100S	40*	30	2	6
2N2459	NPN Si	Lo PA	400	60	50	275S	20*	1	.002	80
2N2460	NPN Si	Lo PA	400	60	50	275S	35*	1	.002	80
2N2461	NPN Si	Lo PA	400	60	50	275S	70*	1	.002	80
2N2462	NPN Si	Lo PA	400	60	50	275S	100*	1	.002	80
2N2463	NPN Si	Lo PA	500	60	50	275S	20*	1	.002	80
2N2464	NPN Si	Lo PA	500	60	50	275S	35*	1	.002	80
2N2465	NPN Si	Lo PA	500	60	50	275S	70*	1	.002	80
2N2466	NPN Si	Lo PA	500	60	50	275S	100*	1	.002	80
2N2467	PNP	A Pwr	5W	30	3A	110S	20*	1A	10ma	60
2N2468	PNP	A Pwr	5W	60	3A	110S	20*	1A	10ma	100
2N2469	PNP	A Pwr	5W	100	3A	110S	20*	1A	10ma	200
2N2472	NPN	Ampl	1W	100	1A	175S	30*	200	50	120
2N2473	NPN	Ampl	1W	100	1A	175S	30*	200	50	120
2N2474	PNP	Lo PA	250	15	50	160	8*	0.1	.001	30
2N2476	NPN	Sw	600	20		300S	20*	150	0.2	30
2N2477	NPN	Sw	600	20	500	300S	40*	150	0.2	30
2N2478	NPN	Sw	600	40	500	175	30*	150	2	60
2N2479	NPN	Sw	600	40	500	175	30*	150	4	40

BASIC TRANSISTOR CIRCUITS

We will now cover a group of basic transistor circuits. These circuits are nothing more than their vacuum-tube counterparts with component values adjusted to compensate for the different characteristics of transistors. The principles of operation of the basic transistor circuit and its vacuum-tube counterpart are similar, and even the circuits resemble each other quite closely. Although the circuits shown are basic, the variations of these circuits found in use can be understood just as easily as can these circuits.

The Multivibrator

This astable, or free-running, multivibrator (see Fig. 3–19) is a square-wave generator. Multivibrators can be used as pulse generators, and with the simple addition of a suitable charging capacitor, a multivibrator can be used to produce a sawtooth waveform, such as that used in TV-set and oscilloscope-sweep circuits. The transistor multivibrator is analagous to the vacuum-tube multivibrator, with various component values changed to compensate for much lower base-input resistance than the input resistance of a tube. Nevertheless, both circuits operate on the same principle. A two-stage, resistance-coupled amplifier in which feedback is deliberately applied from the output of one stage back into the input of the other stage oscillates, providing the proper phase relationships exist.

Although a multivibrator will oscillate by itself, sometimes a synchronizing pulse is applied to it to keep the pulse output in step with a trigger of some sort. Multivibrators can also be used as frequency dividers, such as in frequency-counter circuits. The frequency of the transistor multivibrator is established primarily by base resistors Rb1, Rb2 and coupling capacitors C1 and C2. If Rb1 = Rb2 and C1 = C2, the output will be a pulse train resembling a square wave; the output will be "off" for the same amount of time that it is "on."

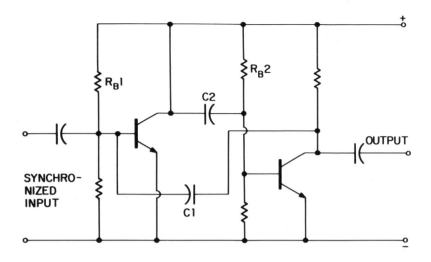

Fig. 3-19. The multivibrator (astable).

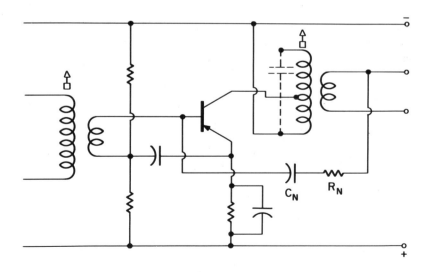

Fig. 3-20. IF amplifier.

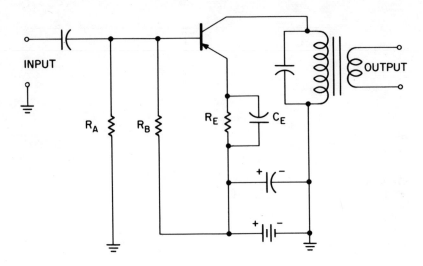

Fig. 3-21. Power amplifier.

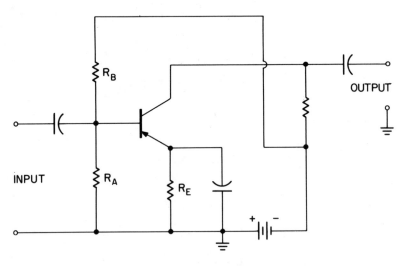

Fig. 3-22. Audio preamplifier.

Variations of this circuit tend to compensate for the sloppy rise and fall times, and some variations introduce diodes to prevent "latch-up," a condition that sometimes occurs when the multivibrator is first turned on, where both outputs (the outputs from the collectors of both transistors) are of low voltage, preventing any oscillation. Normally, when the collector of one transistor is high, the collector of the other transistor is low. Just as with vacuum tubes, the transistors in a transistor multivibrator must have sufficient gain and frequency response to perform satisfactorily.

The IF Amplifier

The intermediate-frequency (IF) amplifier stage (see Fig. 3–20) is used in almost all AM and FM receivers. Again, there is a very close resemblance to the vacuum-tube circuit, with the difference this time being the need for neutralization capacitors in the transistor circuit. Junction capacitances are much greater than the interelectrode capacitances of vacuum tubes and, as such, tend to provide a good feedback path for the transistor unless corrected. To prevent oscillation of the transistor, C_N and R_N are added to this circuit just as they would be placed in a corresponding triode amplifier circuit. C_N is adjusted to cause the feedback voltage to be out of phase with the voltage developed in the $C_N R_N$ leg of the circuit.

Because transistors have low-impedance inputs, the IF transformers encountered in transistor IF strips are of a different type from those found in vacuum-tube IF strips. This is necessary to achieve the maximum transfer of energy.

The Power Amplifier

The typical power amplifier, shown in Fig. 3–21, can be found in the audio-output stages of AM and FM radios, TV sets, and high-fidelity equipment. The transistor circuit for the power amplifier is similar to a vacuum-tube, power-amplifier circuit with differences only in component values and applied biases. The power amplifier is biased into class A conditions through the bias battery and resistors R_A and R_B. Negative dc feedback, provided by the use of resistor R_E, follows the same principles involved in the application of negative feedback through a cathode resistor in vacuum-tube circuits. The output of the transistor is taken from the collector and fed to the primary of an audio-output transformer, which provides the proper impedances to match the transistor to the output load.

The Audio Preamplifier

Figure 3–22 illustrates a single-stage, resistance-coupled, common-emitter voltage amplifier used in phonograph amplifiers and other pieces of audio equipment. The common-emitter configuration not only provides a high-voltage amplification but also creates a power gain. Voltage gains are typically about 100. As in the case of the power amplifier, base bias is set by resistors R_A, R_B, and the emitter resistor R_E. The emitter resistor is again bypassed by a capacitor to prevent the ac signal, which is amplified, from developing a voltage across R_E and thus shifting the operating point.

The Crystal Oscillator

The crystal-oscillator circuit, shown in Fig. 3–23, can be used in transmitters, communications receivers, signal generators, and calibrating test instruments. Figure 3–23 illustrates a collector-tuned, common-base crystal oscillator. The voltage divider consisting of resistors R_A and R_B sets the emitter bias and also determines the collector voltage. R_A and R_B are chosen with low enough resistances to be able to stabilize the emitter and collector currents.

Coil L and capacitor C in the collector circuit form a resonating circuit when C is properly tuned for resonance at the crystal frequency. The ac voltage developed across the tank

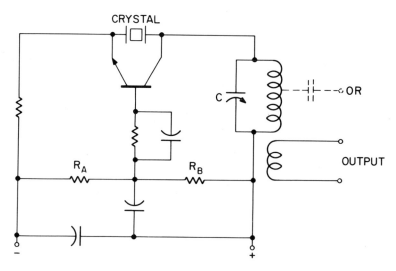

Fig. 3-23. Crystal oscillator.

circuit can then be coupled to an output circuit by means of a coil link (as indicated on the diagram) or a capacitor (shown in dotted lines on the diagram). This crystal-oscillator circuit is very reliable, and the highest frequency at which it will oscillate depends on the crystal type and the transistor–cut-off frequency.

The AND Circuit

The advantages of transistorized gates rather than diode gates are the power-amplification capabilities and isolation properties of transistors. The transistor AND gate (see Fig. 3–24a) is nothing more than a series arrangement of two or more transistors. When neither input or only one of the inputs is applied, the output voltage is equal to the full value of the negative supply voltage. The reason is that no load current is flowing through resistor R_L because there is no current path from the collector of Q1 to ground. When both inputs are applied, however, transistors Q1 and Q2 conduct, thus com-

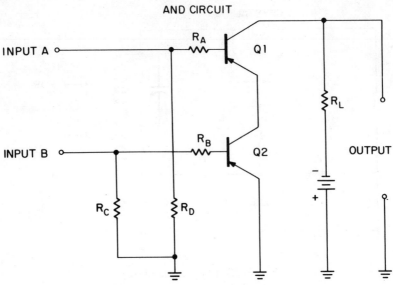

Fig. 3-24a. The AND circuit.

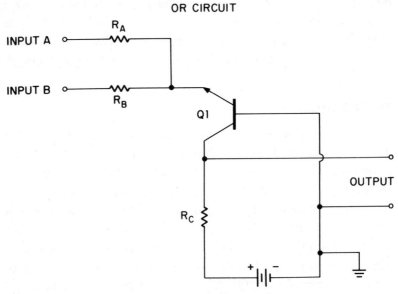

Fig. 3-24b. The OR circuit.

pleting the path from the Q1 collector to ground. This causes current to flow in the collector of Q1 (and Q2) and, therefore, through R_L. The voltage drop across R_L when subtracted from the supply voltage usually leaves an output voltage of a few tenths of a volt.

Since the transistors used are pnp transistors, negative inputs must be applied to cause transistors Q1 and Q2 to conduct. Since the output voltage is about zero for the negative inputs and is about the same as the negative load voltage for other (more positive) inputs, this gate also inverts. Resistors R_A, R_B, R_C, and R_D provide the necessary current-limiting to prevent Q1 and Q2 from going too far into saturation, as this tends to cause delays in the circuit response time. Notice that if pulse inputs are used, the negative inputs must be applied simultaneously to cause the gate to give a true output, for reasons discussed under the topic of diode gates.

The OR Gate

If a negative input is applied to inputs A and/or B of the OR gate (see Fig. 3–24b), the base-emitter junction of transistor Q1 becomes forward-biased. This causes Q1 to conduct, allowing current to flow through R_C and dropping the output voltage from a positive voltage to ground, or slightly negative, depending upon the values of R_A, R_B, and the input voltages. Usually the OR circuit is designed to generate about 0 V in this case. The advantage of the OR circuit is that it does not invert the input signal. That is, a high input will produce a high output (equal to the value of the power-supply voltage), and a low input will produce a low-output voltage (ground). Notice that negative logic (inversion gates), though requiring a readjustment in thinking procedures, is more popular today than noninverting logic. In most cases, the point of input application is all that need be changed to cause a circuit to perform an inverse function.

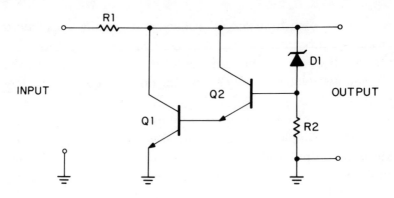

Fig. 3-25. Voltage regulator.

The Voltage Regulator

The voltage regulator, shown in Fig. 3–25, receives an input from an unregulated line of a higher voltage than the desired regulated output voltage. Regulators of this type are used in power supplies for oscillators, computers, and various other equipment requiring a stable voltage.

The voltage across R1 varies, depending on the load requirements. The voltage that biases the Q1–Q2 series combination of transistors is correspondingly changed by this variation, and as a result, the transistors change their loading on the output line. The net effect is to keep a constant voltage at the output line. Zener diode D1 maintains a constant voltage from the base to the collector of Q2, and the voltage developed across R2 is the output voltage minus this zener-diode voltage. Sometimes a temperature compensating diode is placed in series with D1 to assure a more stable voltage output. This is because as the temperature changes, the characteristics of the transistors change, and an internal temperature change for a transistor is caused by a current change.

CHAPTER IV

Troubleshooting Diodes and Their Circuits

In this chapter, we will explore the how and why of diode-circuit servicing. The difference between the serviceman who is successful and the one who is not lies in his approach. A logical and systematic approach is essential to the servicing and troubleshooting of vacuum-tube diode circuits and here as well. Although there are specialized types of diodes, we will be dealing only with those encountered in the electronic circuits discussed in this book.

One of the means of troubleshooting, which has subconsciously developed, is troubleshooting through the use of our senses. Our eyes can spot a charred resistor or see a wisp of smoke rising; our noses can determine excessive heat or detect a component that is "cooking." Our fingers can feel whether a component is too cold (no current flow) or too hot (too much current flow). Our ears can listen for signs of activity, good or bad, such as "singing" noises which could indicate oscillation. With experience, you depend to a great extent on these senses, as most experts do. In addition, our reasoning processes are extremely important in helping to pinpoint trouble.

CHECKING ELECTRONIC CIRCUITS

To troubleshoot any electronic circuit successfully, we must know how to check it out. By use of an appropriate test and an analysis of the test results, we can determine whether a component is defective or not. The method of approach calls for a series of checks in a specific sequence, which can provide the answers we seek. At each step along the way, we must first determine what we are trying to do. This can be done by asking a series of questions such as:

1. Why do we suspect this stage?
2. What are we checking for?
3. What instrument should we use?
4. What readings should we get between what points?
5. Are the poles of the meter properly connected?
6. What precautions should we take before starting?

This list is not final; it simply serves as a basis from which to begin the check. We may decide to add, delete, or modify a question. The choice is ours, because we are the ones to make the decision. Our point is that your approach should be one in which you ask yourself a question and then answer it satisfactorily before proceeding.

Try this method of checking on various circuits before making changes. Repeat the steps again and again until you know them from memory. After a while, they will come easily. The questions allow you to organize your thinking; the checks you make, based on your questions, reveal what you want to know. These questions should set a process in motion which will either move you elsewhere in your testing or halt you until you can determine whether a component is defective at a given point.

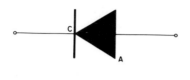

CURRENT FLOW ⟶

Fig. 4-1. Symbol for the basic diode.

Testing Diodes

Before you proceed to check out the diode circuits described in Chapter II, you should know a little about the
diodes being used and the tests that determine whether a diode
is good or not. The basic diode is represented by its symbol in
Fig. 4–1. The direction of current flow is also indicated. If we
take an ohmmeter and place it across the diode, we are either
going to reverse-bias it or forward-bias it, because an ohmmeter uses a battery in its circuitry to check resistance.

Diodes should exhibit a very low resistance when forward-
biased and a very high resistance when reverse-biased. If we
place the negative lead of our ohmmeter on the c terminal and
the positive (probe) lead on the p terminal, we will be forward-biasing it, so we should expect a very low resistance reading. If we reverse the test leads, we should expect an extremely
high resistance reading. The type of diode used determines the
readings, but as a general rule, the low reading is between 15
and 200 Ω (ohms), and the high reading is between 200,000 Ω
and infinity. If the ohmmeter reads 0 Ω, the diode is shorted.
By the way, this test can also be used to determine the polarity
of a diode when it is not marked. We simply place the ohmmeter across the diode, and when it is forward-biased, the
negative lead will indicate the cathode of the diode. Remember
that some ohmmeter manufacturers do not connect the positive
battery terminal to the positive jack of the meter (and the
negative battery terminal to the negative jack of the meter).

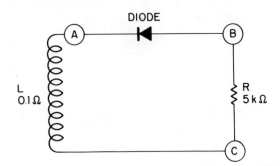

Fig. 4-2. Diode wired in circuit.

Thus, it is wise to know the polarity orientation of the meter before taking these diode-resistance measurements. To check the meter, we use the information we have just gotten—the negative lead of the ohmmeter placed on the cathode and the positive lead of the ohmmeter placed on the anode of the diode will yield a low resistance, between 15 and 200 Ω (on the R times 1 scale or the R times 10 scale).

Now, how do we go about checking the diode to see if it is good or bad? In Fig. 4–2 we show a diode wired up in circuit. Looking at this diagram, we immediately ascertain the polarity of the diode and the manner in which it is wired up. Let us use the method of approach mentioned at the beginning of this chapter and follow a self-questioning checking proce-·dure:

Q. How do we determine whether this diode is good or bad?

A. By the use of an ohmmeter as we did previously. We place the ohmmeter across points A and B, point A being the negative lead of the meter. By doing this, we are forward-biasing the diode and should expect a low ohmmeter reading. This, in fact, is what we find. The ohmmeter reads 15 Ω, which indicates that we have made a correct assumption. This diode is good in the forward-biased condition. However, we still do not know whether the diode is good in the reverse-biased condition.

Q. How do we test the diode in the reverse-biased condition?

A. By the use of an ohmmeter again. This time, however, we must reverse the test leads. When the ohmmeter leads are reversed, the resistance indicated is 5000 Ω, which is not the very high reading we might have expected but is correct. We get the 5000-Ω reading because, although resistor R and inductor L are in series with each other, both together are actually wired across the diode. An ohmmeter always indicates the lowest path for current to flow, and therefore we get a 5000-Ω reading. It is impossible to test a diode properly when it is in a circuit where parallel resistors or coils are wired across it. In order to test it successfully, we must isolate it from any external lead, and this means disconnecting one lead from the circuit. Therefore, we disconnect one lead and take a reading again. This time resistance reads 250,000 Ω, confirming our theory. Let us go back to the checks and see what would happen if R or L were open.

Q. If we place the ohmmeter across the diode in the forward-biased direction, will we still get the same reading as before?

A. We should. In fact, when we conduct this test, we do.

Q. If we place the ohmmeter across the diode in the reverse-biased direction, will we still get the same reading as before?

A. No. If either L or R is open, the ohmmeter will not read 5000 Ω but 250,000 Ω, which is the reverse-biased reading of the diode. When we perform this test in this way, we not only check the diode but the other components as well.

This is how to check out a diode or its associated circuit. In checking out the diode, we must be prepared to include, in all our calculations, any resistors or coils that may be in that circuit. Actually, had we carefully examined this circuit, we could have determined all the possibilities and implications of our test readings, which could then have helped us to pinpoint the defect. What we did was an exercise in troubleshooting, which served to demonstrate the procedure we recommend, a procedure based on questioning ourselves, testing, and getting and analyzing the results.

Specific Troubleshooting Techniques

To make this method of troubleshooting absolutely clear, we are going to examine the diode circuits described in Chapter II, in terms of how to go about troubleshooting them. We will take all schematics included in Chapter II and add identifying points to them so that our troubleshooting procedures will run smoothly. Schematics will include an AM detector, a half-wave rectifier, a full-wave rectifier, a voltage doubler, a bridge rectifier, an FM discriminator, a TV-video detector, an AND circuit, an OR circuit, a damping circuit, and upper and lower clamp circuits.

AM Detector. In looking at the schematic in Fig. 4–3 of an AM detector, we see a similarity between it and our test troubleshooting circuit. Now, where do we start? If we assume nothing, we will make no mistakes. We will proceed in exactly the same way as before, by checking the diode first. Let us connect our ohmmeter across points A and B and again connect the negative lead of the ohmmeter to point A. What should the reading be? A very low value because we are forward-biasing it. The reading on the meter indicates 0 Ω. Would this be correct? It would not. We said low, not zero. This zero reading means that the diode is shorted, and this, then, is the defect in the circuit. If, on the other hand, the meter reads 100 Ω, we would assume that the diode is good in the forward-biased condition, and by reversing the ohmmeter leads, we would expect a very high reading.

The tests on this circuit are almost identical to those performed in our exercise, but we are using a 50,000-Ω resistor instead of a 5000-Ω resistor. Remember, a test of any diode, in

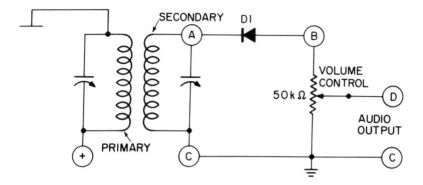

Fig. 4-3. AM detector.

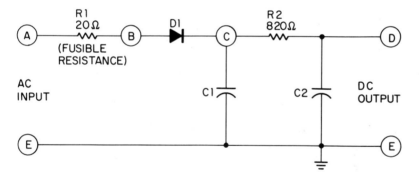

Fig. 4-4. Half-wave rectifier.

most cases, will not only check the diode but its external circuitry as well. We must know what ohmmeter readings to expect when we test the diode by forward or reverse-biasing it. The rest comes naturally and shows up easily.

Half-wave Rectifier. In Fig. 4–4 is a typical schematic of a half-wave rectifier which is found in most transistorized

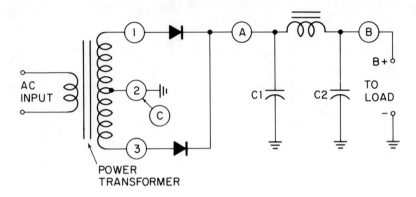

Fig. 4-5. Full-wave rectifier.

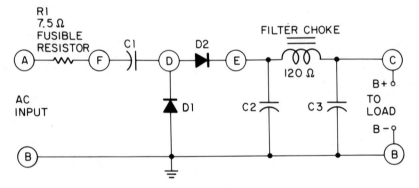

Fig. 4-6. Voltage doubler.

radios, phonographs, and TV sets. It is thus very desirable to know how to check it out. The value of resistors or capacitors may vary, depending upon their use, but the troubleshooting techniques do not. Let us check the diode and all of the important circuitry first. By placing our ohmmeter across points A and D, we can determine whether R1, D1, and R2 are open.

We must remember, however, which leads go where. The cathode (B plus) connection should go to the negative lead of the ohmmeter, in order to set the forward-biased condition; by placing the negative lead on point D, we maintain this condition.

The next step is to determine what meter reading to expect when we do this. We refer to the schematic and find that we have R1 (20 Ω) in series with D1 (very low resistance) and in series with R2 (820 Ω). We add R1, R2, and D1 (estimated) to arrive at approximately 850–950 Ω. Having estimated what we should read on the ohmmeter, we now place the ohmmeter across these points and obtain a reading of 920 Ω. This means that there is no open circuit, *i.e.*, nothing burnt out.

The next step is to check the diode itself in both the forward and reverse directions. We should obtain the readings we got previously. If we do not, this indicates that the diode is defective and must be replaced. However, before connecting it to the ac supply, we must determine if the diode went bad by itself or whether some external device caused it to go bad. An ohmmeter check from point E (negative lead) to point D (positive lead) tells us if CI or C2 are shorted. If they are not shorted, we can apply power, and dc voltage should appear across D and E. The replacement of any component should always be followed by checking to determine if the component itself went bad, or some externally wired component caused it to go bad. This is always done by the simple expedient of an ohmmeter check before power is applied.

Full-wave Rectifier. Figure 4–5 is a schematic of a full-wave rectifier using power diodes. We start troubleshooting this power supply by disconnecting it from the ac source. Then we use the ohmmeter. A check of each diode can be made, in the same way as before, but in this case, each diode must be checked out of the circuit, since all the diodes are in parallel with one another. A resistance check between A and B will determine if the choke is open or not and will show up a short circuit across B and C if C1 or C2 is shorted.

There are not so many components that we cannot check out each one separately, if we wish to do so. If the defective component is found, replace it, and then always place an ohmmeter across B and C just to make sure that there is no short, before you apply power. An ohmmeter can also be used to check the transformer windings. It should be obvious by now that the ohmmeter is one of the best test instruments to use in troubleshooting diodes and their associated circuitry.

Voltage Doubler. Again, as in all previous instances, we use an ohmmeter to check the voltage doubler (see Fig. 4–6). A dc voltmeter is always used to check voltage, after we have found the problem and corrected it. In this schematic we have marked off A through F test points. Now check it out and run through the procedures. When finished, check it out against this check list:

1. Ohmmeter across A and F should read 7.5 Ω.
2. Ohmmeter across E and C should read 120 Ω.
3. Ohmmeter across A and B should read infinity.
4. Ohmmeter across C and D, depending upon polarity, should read 130–200 Ω, or more than 200,000 Ω.
5. Ohmmeter across D and B should read 10–150 Ω, or more than 200,000 Ω.

These are the correct readings, and we should go over the schematic to see how they were arrived at. This is what we mean when we talk about analyzing a circuit and arriving at the values. A crucial aspect of troubleshooting involves taking the time to estimate the readings which should be obtained, analyzing the actual readings measured, and comparing them with our estimate. We cannot stress this process enough, since our ultimate goal is to help you develop organized trouble-shooting techniques—these stem from organized thinking.

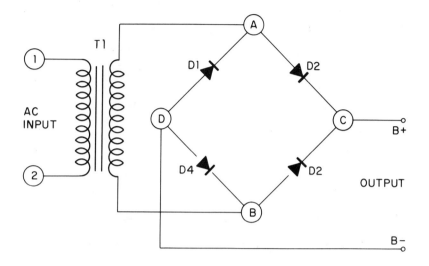

Fig. 4-7. Bridge rectifier circuit.

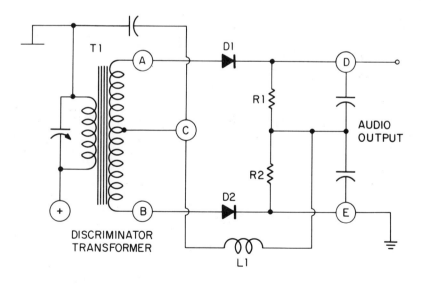

Fig. 4-8. FM discriminator.

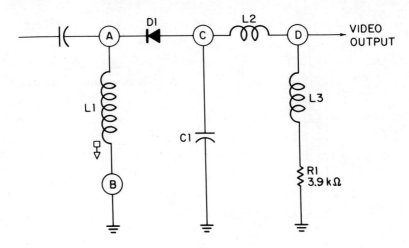

Fig. 4-9. Video detector.

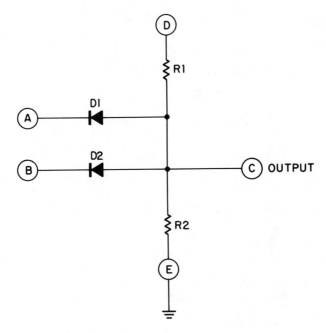

Fig. 4-10. The AND circuit.

Bridge-rectifier Circuit. Before we start troubleshooting, let us start by examining this bridge rectifier (see Fig. 4–7). Notice the way in which the diodes are wired. A careful look shows why analysis is a must in this schematic. The checking of any specific diode must take into account the fact that there may be other diodes wired in parallel with it as well as the secondary winding of T1. Therefore, each diode must be removed from the circuit in order to be tested. Remember that with the ohmmeter tests, forward and reverse-biasing give different readings. First, we estimate the expected reading and then use the ohmmeter to check it out. If the obtained reading does not agree with the estimated reading, a defective component is suspected. It may also be that we did not estimate properly. In any case, a re-check is in order.

Discriminator. This discriminator circuit (see Fig. 4–8) can be checked out easily, and the procedure is the same one used in the other circuits. Estimate the various resistances to be obtained and then compare them with resistances actually obtained when checked. If there is a discrepancy, look for the reason. This time, in checking out this circuit, certain assumptions will be made. We will assume that you know that an ohmmeter between A and D checks diode D1 and that an ohmmeter between B and E checks D2. Now, what does an ohmmeter between A and B check? The answer is the secondary of transformer T1. Did you know? If not, examine the circuit. What reading should an ohmmeter between D and E give? What happens if we reverse our leads? The answer to both questions is the same—the value of R1 and R2. Remember, when we place the ohmmeter across D and E, only one diode will be forward-biased, and when we reverse the ohmmeter leads, the other diode will be forward-biased. Since both diodes are in series but back to back, the resistance reading across D and E will always be the reading we expect from one diode when in the reverse diode condition. Since this resistance is very high, we can ignore it in relation to the resistance of R1 and R2 in series because they have a much lower resistance. If an ohmmeter between D and E gives a reading of 7 Ω, what might the cause be? One diode could be shorted, which would prevent it from operating properly under the reverse-biased condition.

Video Detector. The correct procedure for the video detector (see Fig. 4–9) dictates that we first estimate the ohmmeter readings across points A, B, C, and D. The ohmmeter when placed between B (negative) and D should give us a reading of approximately 100–200 Ω. Let us see how we arrive at this estimate. In this condition the ohmmeter places a forward bias on D1, through L1. We must assume certain resistance readings. We will assume resistances for L1 and L2, which, in video circuits, are small coils. Therefore, we assume a resistance of approximately 5 Ω for each, which could be wrong, but not too far off the mark. This means that L1, D1, and L2 are in series, and if we assume 5 Ω for L1, 100 Ω for D1, and 5 Ω for L2, we should obtain a reading of 110 Ω. If we then, after estimating the reading, go through the process of checking the ohmmeter and get a reading of 90–200 Ω, this would still be correct.

Remember, estimating need not be accurate. A defective component alters the reading drastically. We are only trying to determine whether the diode and coils are good. Were we to reverse the ohmmeter leads, the diode would be reverse-biased, and we should expect a reading of 3900 Ω. The reasoning is as follows. If the diode is biased in the reverse direction, the ohmmeter would indicate a very high resistance, except that R1 and L3 are in parallel with L1, D1, and L2. The ohmmeter always indicates the lowest reading, which, in this case, is R1 plus L3, or 3900 Ω plus 5 Ω, or 3905 Ω. The guess of 3900 Ω is a good one.

AND Circuit. The AND circuit (see Fig. 4–10) is checked

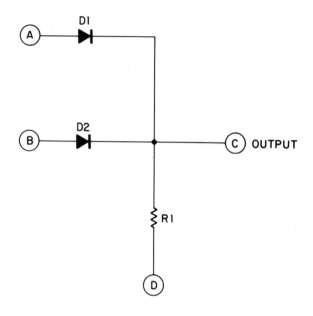

Fig. 4-11. The OR circuit.

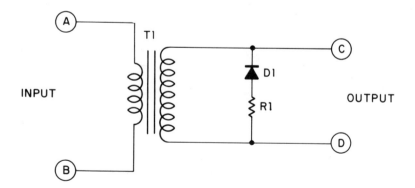

Fig. 4-12. Damping circuit.

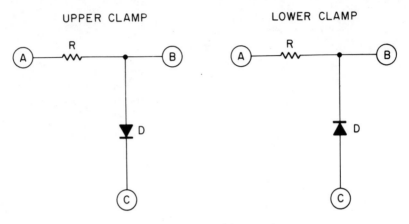

Fig. 4-13. Upper and lower clamps.

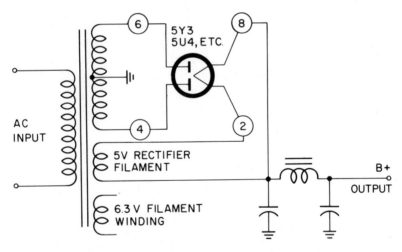

Fig. 4-14. Vacuum-tube rectifier power supply.

using the same procedures as have already been made clear. Check diode D1 by placing the ohmmeter across A and C, check diode D2 by placing the ohmmeter between B and C. In each case, check both forward and reverse bias. R1 or R2 can be checked by using a simple ohmmeter test from D to E.

OR Circuit. The checks of the OR circuit (see Fig. 4–11) should be made exactly as in the AND circuit, with one exception—R1 is checked by placing the ohmmeter between C and D and D1 and D2, as indicated in Fig. 4–10.

Damping Circuit. In the damping circuit (see Fig. 4–12), D1 must be removed from the circuit in order to test it properly, because the winding of T1 is in parallel across it and would give an erroneous reading. All other components should be tested while the diode is disconnected, for more accurate resistance readings.

Upper and Lower Clamp. The clamps (see Fig. 4–13) can be checked simply. To check R, we must put the ohmmeter between A and B; to check the diode, we must connect the ohmmeter between B and C. Note the polarity of these diodes and check them accordingly.

We have tried to show you, in this section, how easy it is to troubleshoot a diode and its circuit. We have emphasized the need to analyze a circuit and the importance of estimating the expected results. It should be obvious that the ohmmeter is the basic instrument used to test diodes and their circuits. Our intention has been to convince you that testing a solid-state diode can be easily accomplished. The basic tools, the basic techniques, and the basic procedures have been pointed out and elaborated upon in this chapter.

SERVICE PROBLEMS OF RECTIFIERS

The remaining portion of this chapter contains information that is especially helpful to the serviceman. It deals with the application of silicon rectifiers as replacements and modifications of existing equipment.

In most cases a silicon rectifier can be used to replace a selenium or vacuum-tube rectifier in order to utilize the advantages of the silicon rectifier. A solid-state rectifier does not need a filament supply since it does not have a filament or heater.

It does not generate heat because it has an extremely low internal loss; this also means that more voltage is available to the equipment, for the same line-source voltage. Heat, generated by a vacuum-tube rectifier, causes a premature breakdown of components that may be mounted nearby. The solid-state rectifier does not deteriorate with age or use and, therefore, will last the life of the equipment. It is so small that it can be installed in any convenient spot either above or below the chassis.

Selenium and vacuum-tube rectifiers deteriorate with use and age and thus require periodic replacement. Not only do they deteriorate, but they become leaky, gassy, and permit ac through them. This causes damage to other components. Therefore, silicon rectifiers should replace these older types of rectifier devices. In this section we will examine a few of the basic selenium and vacuum-tube rectifier circuits and will show how easy it is to use silicon rectifiers as replacements for them.

Replacing a Vacuum-Tube Rectifier

Let us start with a basic vacuum-tube rectifier power supply as shown in Fig. 4–14. Notice that we have marked off the pin connections of the rectifier tube on the schematic. In this circuit the rectifier tube is a full-wave rectifier; this means that we must use two silicon rectifiers as replacements. Figure 4–15 shows how we can do this, eliminating the need for the filament supply. We can either cut off the filament supply leads at the tube socket or leave them connected.

If we use the rectifier tube socket pins as tie points for the silicon rectifiers, the replacement job is made easy. Now, how do we determine the type of silicon rectifier to use as a replacement for the vacuum-tube rectifier? The silicon rectifier replacement must be able to handle the same current as the rectifier tube and must have the same PIV (peak inverse voltage) rating. In practice, it is wise to select a silicon rectifier

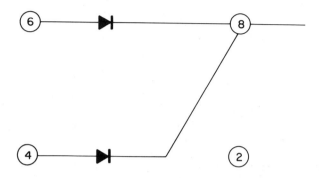

Fig. 4-15. Elimination of the need for filament supply.

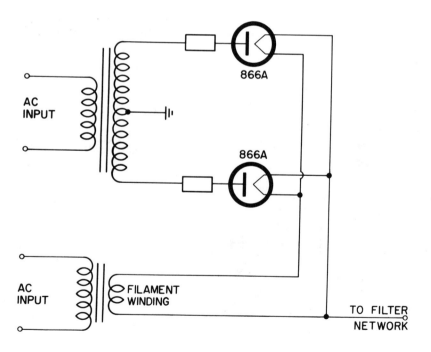

Fig. 4-16. Wiring of two 866A tubes.

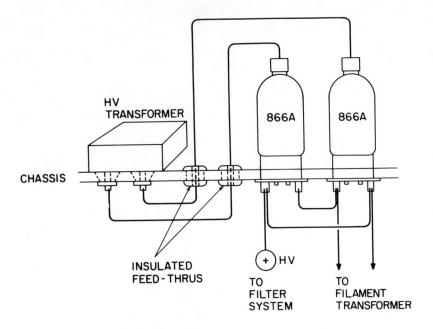

Fig. 4-17. Physical arrangement of two 866A tubes.

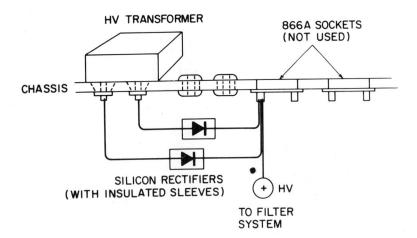

Fig. 4-18. Physical arrangement of two silicon rectifiers.

with a 50 per cent higher rating of both the current and PIV. This insures an adequate safety factor.

Simply make a note of the type of rectifier tube used in the power supply and then search through a tube manual to find the information needed. Assume that the tube we wish to replace is a 5Y3GT. The tube manual indicates that it has a PIV rating of 1400 maximum volts and under "Typical Operation" with a capacitor input supply (which is what our power supply has), we find that the maximum full-load current rating is 150 mA. If we now add our safety factor to these figures, we find that the PIV of the silicon rectifier should be rated at about 2100 V and that it should be able to handle at least 225 mA of current.

Having selected silicon rectifiers that meet or exceed all the specifications, we install them across the tube socket. This completes the conversion process. A sticker should be placed over the tube socket as a reminder not to attempt to install a rectifier tube. It should be noted on the sticker that silicon rectifiers have been installed as replacements for the rectifier tube and are wired across the bottom of the rectifier-tube socket. It is important to indicate to other servicemen, for example, that modification of the power supply has been made.

If we do not want to select and install our own silicon diodes, we can purchase a rectifier-tube silicon replacement that plugs right into the 5Y3 tube socket. This might seem like a better idea, but it is not. These replacement rectifiers are not made for a specific tube type but as general replacements. Actually, to be sure that the replacement silicon diodes have the correct specifications for a reasonable safety factor, we must select them ourselves. Furthermore, it is usually cheaper to choose them ourselves.

Replacing a Mercury-Vapor Rectifier

Many transmitter power supplies use the 866A mercury-vapor type of rectifier tube. These are used because they have a very low internal loss. Unfortunately, they are short-lived and create an annoying "hash" noise, which gets into the equipment. In this instance, a silicon-rectifier device is not only able to replace the tube but has none of its disadvantages.

Let us now examine the current and PIV ratings of the mercury-vapor tube to determine the silicon-rectifier replacement. If we look up the 866A tube in a transmitting tube manual, we will see that the current rating is the same as that of the low-voltage rectifiers. In Fig. 4–16, two 866A's are wired in a manner similar to the low-voltage rectifier power supplies. The only difference is that two tubes are used here, each one a half-wave rectifier. A special filament transformer is also used for the 866A's, which is insulated for high voltage.

Figure 4–17 indicates the physical layout that is normally used with these 866A's. Remove the 866A's and the two plate leads by cutting them off at the high-voltage transformer terminals. Also, remove the filament transformer and disconnect its leads and then install the silicon rectifiers as shown in Fig. 4–18. Extreme care must be used when installing these diodes; they must be placed well away from each other, any components, and the chassis itself. High-voltage plastic sleeves should be slipped over each silicon rectifier as an extra precaution.

As with the 5Y3 tube, there is a power-rectifier silicon replacent made for 866A's, which will plug into the tube socket. These units eliminate the necessity for removing the plate caps and leads, since they have a plate cap on top of them. Whichever way we wish to do it, the silicon rectifiers are a perfect replacement for the 866A tube.

Replacing a Selenium Rectifier

Silicon rectifiers can replace selenium rectifiers. However, the same specifications must be met. Figure 4–19 shows the circuit of a typical selenium-rectifier type of power supply,

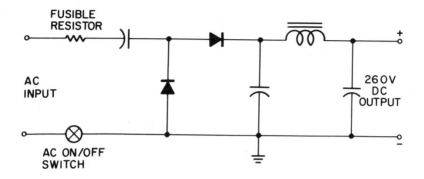

Fig. 4-19. Typical selenium-rectifier circuit.

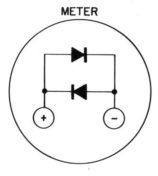

Fig. 4-20. Two silicon-diode rectifiers wired across meter terminals.

which was used in many of the older TV sets. Even though the most recent TV sets use silicon rectifiers, there are still many older models that require updating. The selenium rectifier is a circuit of a popular voltage doubler, which does not use a power transformer. The fusible resistor, used here as a current-limiting device, must not be removed from the circuit. As in all other circuits, we must look up both the current and PIV ratings before we install the silicon diodes. To get the information on

Fig. 4-21a. Silicon rectifiers in series arrangement.

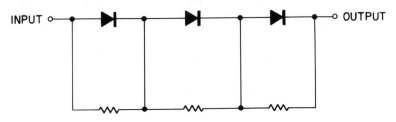

Fig. 4-21b. A 500,000-Ω, 0.5-W resistor across each of three diodes.

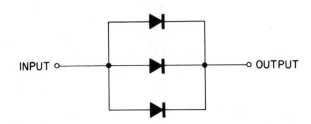

Fig. 4-22a. Silicon rectifiers in parallel arrangement.

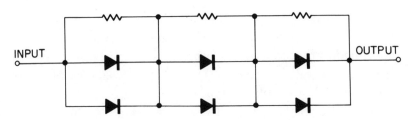

Fig. 4-22b. Series and parallel silicon diodes with equalizing resistors.

these selenium rectifiers, we can use the manufacturer's parts replacement list for the TV set. Then, we must select suitable silicon replacements and install them.

Preventing Meter Damage

Another application of diodes is in circuitry for the protection of a test volt-ohmmeter. With the meter scale multiplier set to a low value and the test leads inadvertently placed across a high-voltage source, damage to the meter could easily result. The meter would react so violently that either the meter movement would burn out or the needle would be bent very badly. In Fig. 4–20, two silicon-diode rectifiers are wired across the meter terminals to prevent meter damage. If a voltage in excess of 0.7 V were to appear across the meter terminals, one of these silicon diodes would conduct, shunting the current around the meter, and no permanent damage to the meter or to its movement would occur. The silicon diodes are the same type as those used in power-rectifier applications.

If a multimeter has a meter with an internal resistance of 1200 Ω and a full-scale rating of 50 μA, these silicon rectifiers would introduce a meter error of less than 1 per cent. The silicon diodes would limit the maximum current through the meter to less than 1 mA (0.001 A), if the current surge were to reach 1.0 A. This is a perfect protective device for any volt-ohmmeter. Again, there is a unit already made expressly for those who do not wish to install silicon rectifiers.

Installing Silicon Rectifiers in Series and in Parallel

Silicon rectifiers may be used as replacements even if their PIV ratings are low. They may be installed in a series arrangement as shown in Fig. 4–21a. When installed in this way, simply add the PIV rating of each diode—this total is the PIV rating of the entire series string. We can use two, three, or as many as necessary to attain the required PIV rating. When semiconductor diodes are used in a series arrangement, each diode may be slightly different from another. It is possible that the voltage will divide unequally across the diodes. A diode with too much voltage across it may then short out and cause all the others to fail. A simple way to equalize the voltage drops across the diodes is to put a 500,000-Ω, 0.5-W resistor across each of them as shown in Fig. 4–21b.

Silicon rectifiers, which have a lower current rating than the device they replace, may also be used. They can be installed in a parallel arrangement as shown in Fig. 4–22a. By adding the current rating of each silicon diode, we obtain the total current limit for the group.

Figure 4–22b shows an arrangement of both series and parallel silicon diodes with equalizing resistors, which can be used to provide a specific amount of current at a certain PIV. This method of placing the silicon diode in either a series, parallel, or combination arrangement enables us to meet any requirement of current and/or PIV ratings.

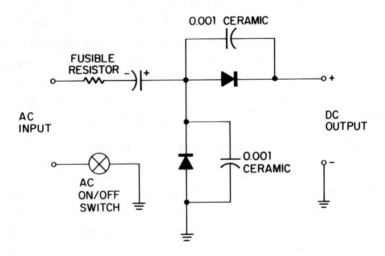

Fig. 4-23. Capacitors set up across the silicon diodes.

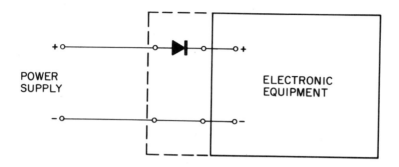

Fig. 4-24. Silicon diode as a switch.

Installing Capacitors and Wiring a Switch

All ac power lines generate high-voltage transients that can destroy silicon rectifiers. There are many ways to cope with this problem, but the best way by far is to add a small capacitor across the silicon diode. Figure 4–23 shows the method of installing these capacitors. The capacitors generally act to shunt the sharp spike of the transient around the diode.

There are simple methods used to prevent blown transistors due to inadvertent polarity reversal of the power supply output to a piece of electronic equipment. Figure 4–24 shows how a silicon diode is wired to act as a switch. When the voltage source is incorrectly connected, the silicon rectifier is reverse-biased and prevents any current flow into the equipment. The silicon diode is connected externally, although it may easily be installed in the equipment as shown by the dotted lines.

CHAPTER V

Troubleshooting Transistor Circuits

Troubleshooting a transistor circuit is not necessarily more difficult than troubleshooting a diode circuit. The reason that troubleshooting a transistor circuit is sometimes more of a problem is that transistors can fail in several ways, instead of the single way diodes can fail, mentioned in diode-circuit troubleshooting.

TRANSISTOR FAILURES

When a transistor fails, we have to ask ourselves why did it fail, in what way did it fail, and did something make it fail or did it fail on its own. These questions, which may appear irrelevant, are really important; they serve as a guide to troubleshooting any transistor circuit.

We mentioned in Chapter III that a transistor can be thought of as being composed of two diodes. Although this is not entirely accurate, it is a great aid to testing transistors and

makes possible transistor troubleshooting with the use of only
a simple ohmmeter. Figure 5–1 illustrates npn and pnp transistors with their diode "equivalent" circuits. One of the ways in
which a transistor fails is when one of its diodes becomes
shorted. This means that if the diode representing the collector-
base junction of an npn transistor (diode A) exhibits the same
low resistance when forward-biased as it does when reverse-
biased, the transistor is defective. The same is true for diodes
B, C, and D. We can check this with an ohmmeter. If we place
the positive lead of the ohmmeter on the base of the npn
transistor and the negative ohmmeter lead on the collector, we
should read a much lower resistance than if we reversed the
ohmmeter leads. This is true because in the first case, we are
measuring the resistance of a forward-biased diode, whereas
in the second case, we are measuring the resistance of a reverse-
biased diode.

Similarly, if we place the positive lead of the ohmmeter on
the base of the npn transistor and the negative ohmmeter lead
on the emitter, we will read a much lower resistance than if
we reverse the ohmmeter leads, assuming that the transistor
is not defective. If the transistor is defective, both resistances
(when forward biasing or reverse biasing with the ohmmeter
leads) will be the same or low (usually, around 100 Ω or less).

Remember again to make sure that the positive lead of
the ohmmeter is connected to the positive ohmmeter battery
terminal (and the same for the negative lead and the battery
terminal) to avoid any confusion about test results later.

NOTE: Check the transistors on an ohmmeter scale where
the open-circuit voltage (between the probes) and the short-
circuit current (through the probes) are limited to below 2 V
and less than about 3 mA respectively. This means that
VTVM's (vacuum-tube voltmeters) should be set to about
R × 1 kV (kilovolt) scale, and VOM's (volt-ohmmeters) should
be set to the R × 10 or R × 100 scale in most cases.

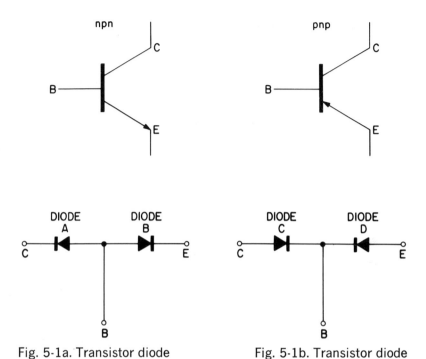

Fig. 5-1a. Transistor diode equivalent circuit.

Fig. 5-1b. Transistor diode equivalent circuit.

Because the pnp transistor has a "reversed" diode equivalent circuit from the npn transistor, we must reverse the ohmmeter leads to obtain the same indication. That is, if the negative lead of the ohmmeter is placed on the base of the pnp transistor and the positive ohmmeter lead is placed on the collector, we will read a much lower resistance than if we reversed the ohmmeter leads. Similarly, if we place the negative lead of the ohmmeter on the base of the pnp transistor and the positive lead on the emitter, we will read a much lower resistance than if we reversed the ohmmeter leads. This is true because forward and reverse biasing are accomplished differently, in regard to polarity, in pnp transistors.

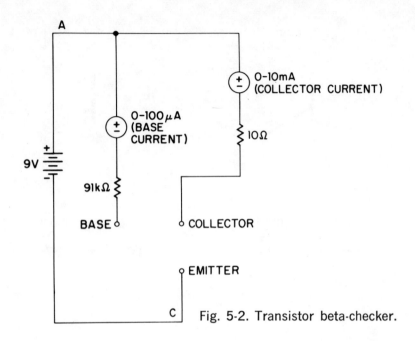

Fig. 5-2. Transistor beta-checker.

Another way in which a transistor fails is when its current gain (alpha or beta) drops to a very low value. In certain circuits, a low beta may not affect circuit operation, but in most cases, if the gain of a transistor is too low, the circuit will not operate. If an amplifier does not have sufficient gain, for example, the output will not be high enough to drive a succeeding amplification stage. This applies to vacuum tubes too. Vacuum tubes are gain-checked by means of a transconductance measurement to ascertain whether the vacuum tube is doing its job. The vacuum-tube equation $\mu = g_m r_p$ (where μ equals the vacuum-tube amplification factor, g_m equals the transconductance, and r_p equals the plate dynamic resistance) can be solved for μ, the vacuum-tube gain, once the transconductance g_m is known, since the amplification is directly proportional to the transconductance.

Measuring beta is easy to do. A circuit given in Fig. 5–2

checks the beta of any npn transistor with only some simple division. To check a pnp transistor for beta, point A should be connected to the negative battery terminal, point C should be connected to the positive battery terminal, and both meters should be polarity-reversed (the positive terminal wired to the point the negative terminal went to and the negative terminal wired to the point the positive terminal went to).

The 0–100 microammeter reads the base current. The 0–10 milliammeter indicates the collector current. If we divide the collector current by the base current, we get beta. It is as easy as that. If we read the collector current while disconnecting the base, we read leakage current I_{CEO}*.

In a good transistor, the leakage current is very small. The minimum acceptable beta values for transistors are given in almost all transistor tables, so a good-fair-poor comparison can easily be made between the manufacturer's information and the transistor tested.

Heat plays an important part in transistor performance. Sometimes the transistor leakage current becomes so great at higher temperatures that the transistor no longer performs satisfactorily. This will show up too when checking leakage with the transistor beta-checker. If the leakage current (base disconnected) increases with time, it is because the collector-emitter junction is heating up. If it increases very rapidly, the transistor is probably useless after it heats up, in circuit operation. Semiconductor-diode leakage current also increases somewhat as the diode junction heats up, but this effect is not as pronounced as leakage in transistors. Needless to say, vacuum tubes have some leakage also.

Before beginning typical circuit-transistor troubleshooting, let us discuss transistor biasing. A transistor conducts if its base-emitter junction is forward-biased while its base-collector junction is reverse-biased. This means, in an npn transistor, that if the base gets some voltage V_B, the emitter gets some voltage

---

* $I_{CEO} = (1 + \beta) I_{CBO}$ described in Chapter III.

V_E, and the collector gets some voltage V_C, then for conduction, $V_E < V_B < V_C$. For a pnp transistor, $V_C < V_B < V_E$. If we ground the emitters of these transistors, as is commonly done, then we can bias these transistors as shown in Fig. 5–3. Resistors R_b are sometimes used to stabilize the transistor-base bias and are between one-tenth and one times the value of the base resistor 50 kΩ (kilohms).

When a germanium transistor is conducting, it has a base-emitter voltage drop of about 0.2 V and a collector-emitter voltage drop of about 0.3 V (when saturated). This is useful to know when trying to find out whether a transistor that is supposed to be on is really on.

We can troubleshoot a transistor circuit in several ways, and the way we choose depends upon how much skill we have. In other words, depending upon the actual transistor circuit, one method of troubleshooting is faster or easier or both than another method of troubleshooting the same circuit. For example, sometimes troubleshooting with a voltmeter (incidentally, we only use VTVM or equivalent voltmeters in troubleshooting transistor circuits) is harder than troubleshooting with an ohmmeter. Why? Because sometimes we do not know what voltage indications we should get at particular circuit points, so we may have to take many voltage readings to pinpoint the circuit malfunction. In some cases, troubleshooting with an ohmmeter is the poorer way to troubleshoot the circuit simply because troubleshooting with a voltmeter is much faster and much more efficient. In other cases, troubleshooting with both an ohmmeter and a voltmeter is the fastest method, using the voltmeter to check some circuit points and using an ohmmeter to check other circuit points, such as resistors.

The beta-checker is used, in some cases, where a reasonably accurate indication of the gain of a transistor is needed. The beta-checker also helps us determine if heat is the source of transistor trouble (through leakage current).

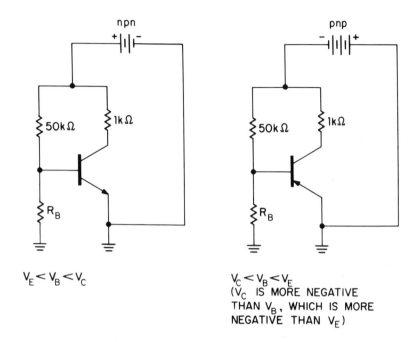

Fig. 5-3. Transistor biasing.

In any case, other tools would help but are not essential, because when the circuit fails, certain obvious effects will be just as obvious with a voltmeter as with an oscilloscope. We are about ready now to troubleshoot the transistor equipment of Chapter III. In summary, we will need a few tools—an ohm-meter, a voltmeter, and a beta-checker. A good transistor hand-book will also help in case there is any doubt as to whether the transistor-gain indication meets or falls below the manufac-turer's ratings, which would cause the transistor gain to fall below most circuit requirements.

TROUBLESHOOTING THE MULTIVIBRATOR

Figure 5–4 illustrates an astable multivibrator with sev-eral key test points. The astable multivibrator is free-running

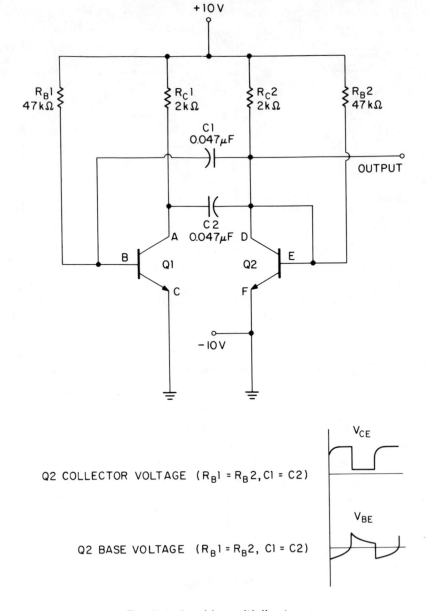

Fig. 5-4. Astable multivibrator.

and outputs a pulse train. If Rb2 = Rb1 and C1 = C2, the pulses will be symmetrical. If this circuit is not working, we can troubleshoot the circuit by performing resistance checks, after disconnecting the collector-supply voltage (10 V dc in this circuit). We start by checking the base-emitter junction of Q1 with an ohmmeter. If we place the positive ohmmeter lead on B and the negative ohmmeter lead on C, we should read a resistance of about 100 Ω. If we reverse the ohmmeter leads, we should read a much greater resistance. If we do not obtain an indication of at least 50 kΩ, preferably about 500 kΩ or so, we can assume that Q1 is defective.

We should then proceed in the same way to check transistor Q2. If we place the positive ohmmeter lead on E and the negative ohmmeter lead on D (this forward bias checks the base-emitter junction of Q2), we should again read a resistance of about 100 Ω. If we reverse the ohmmeter leads, we should again read a much greater resistance (at least 50 kΩ or so). Similarly, if this condition is not met, we should assume that Q2 is defective.

Now we should check the base-collector junction of Q1 with the ohmmeter positive lead on B and the negative lead on A. Since we are checking a forward-biased resistance, we should again get an indication of about 100 Ω. When we reverse the ohmmeter leads, we should read at least 25 kΩ this time. This is because we are checking the resistance of the series combination of Rb1 and RC1 in parallel with the base-collector junction. Rb1 and RC1 in series give us a resistance of about 50 kΩ and the base-collector junction, which is reverse-biased in this case, gives us an indication of at least 50 kΩ. We should, therefore, set the lowest acceptable resistance indication as 25 kΩ. For a more accurate reverse-biased resistance check of the base-collector junction, we should unsolder Q1 and check it without the external circuit influences of the resistors.

If we get an indication of 4-kΩ resistance on the reverse-biased check (with the transistor still in circuit), it probably means that capacitor C1 is shorted because 4 kΩ is the series resistance of RC1 and RC2, which is what the ohmmeter would read if C1 were shorted.

The next step is the checking of the base-collector junction of Q2. We check this by placing the ohmmeter positive lead on E and by placing the negative lead on D. If the resistance measured is about 100 Ω, we should next try checking this junction with the ohmmeter leads reversed. This reverse-biased resistance should be at least 25 kΩ. The 25-kΩ resistance is, this time, the combination of series resistors RC2 and Rb2 in parallel with the reverse-biased resistance of the Q2 base-collector junction. The series-resistance combination should give us an indication of about 49 kΩ, and the base-collector, reverse-biased resistance should yield an indication of much greater than 50 kΩ. We, therefore, set the lowest acceptable resistance indication as about 25 kΩ. Again, a more accurate check of the reverse-biased, base-collector junction can be made by unsoldering the transistor from the circuit and checking the base-collector junction resistance without external circuit influences, and we should get an indication of much greater than 50 kΩ. A 4-kΩ indication probably means that capacitor C2 is shorted, although one should also suspect that the transistor is defective.

If the transistors pass these tests, then the next thing to test is the resistance of all circuit resistors and capacitors, after disconnecting one end of these components from the circuit so that we have eliminated external circuit influences from the measurements. If the components are good, we should remove the transistors and check them with the beta-checker (see Fig. 5–2), which will also check the transistor leakage. This final check will, if nothing else, eliminate the transistors as the cause of the circuit malfunctioning.

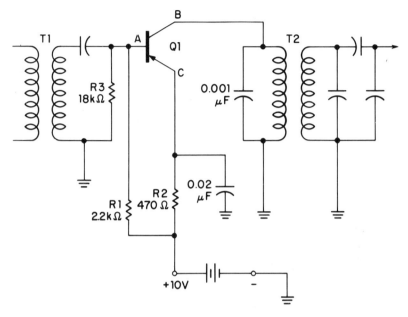

Fig. 5-5. IF amplifier.

TROUBLESHOOTING THE INTERMEDIATE-FREQUENCY AMPLIFIER

·The IF amplifier, shown in Fig. 5–5, illustrates the use of a pnp transistor. If we check this circuit with an ohmmeter, we will probably troubleshoot it in the fastest possible way. We will also gain some experience with the kind of checks we performed in troubleshooting the multivibrator. We should begin by disconnecting the voltage-supply source of 10 V dc. Let us now check the resistance of the forward-biased, base-emitter junction of transistor Q1. Remembering that we forward-bias this junction with the ohmmeter, we place the positive ohmmeter lead on C and the negative ohmmeter lead on A. We

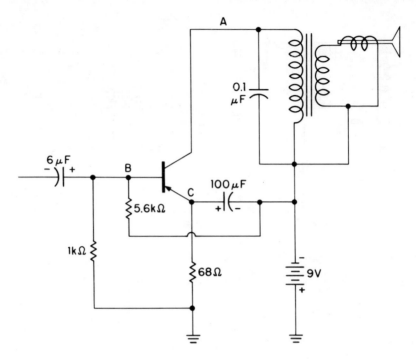

Fig. 5-6. Power amplifier.

should observe a resistance indication of 100 Ω. The reverse-biased resistance check is performed by reversing the ohmmeter leads. The resistance indication we should observe in this test is about 2.7 kΩ, because series resistors R1 and R2, giving us a total resistance of 2.7 kΩ, are in parallel with the junction we are measuring. Therefore, to obtain a useful measurement (we wish to measure a resistance in the range of at least 50 kΩ), we must disconnect either the base or emitter from the rest of the circuit, thus isolating the external circuit influences (resistors R1 and R2). The reverse-biased resistance should then be at least 50 kΩ. If any of these measurements is not verified, we must assume that transistor Q1 is defective and should be replaced.

The next thing to check is the forward-biased resistance of the base-collector junction. We do this by placing the positive ohmmeter lead on B and the negative ohmmeter lead on A. This resistance should be about 100 Ω. Before performing the reverse-bias check, we should notice that there is another current path from the base to the collector. This current path starts at the collector and goes through the primary of transformer T1 to ground and from ground through resistor R3 (18 kΩ) to the base. Therefore, we never read a resistance of greater than 18 kΩ, even if the reverse-biased resistance is greater than 100 kΩ. We must remove the base or collector lead from the rest of the circuit before performing the reverse-biased resistance check. We should then read at least 50 kΩ of resistance. This resistance is checked by placing the positive ohmmeter lead on B (the collector of the transistor) and by placing the negative ohmmeter lead on A (the base). Again, if any of these readings is not obtained, transistor Q1 is shown to be defective and should be replaced.

If the circuit passes these transistor checks, we should next check the remaining circuit components. As a final step, we should again check the transistor with the beta-checker, after first modifying the beta-checker circuit for the testing of pnp transistors. This provides the final test of the transistor, as either a low beta or high leakage current could each cause improper IF amplifier operation.

TROUBLESHOOTING THE POWER AMPLIFIER

Figure 5–6 illustrates a pnp transformer-coupled power amplifier. The circuit illustrated is used to drive a speaker. The 5600-Ω and 1-kΩ resistor form a voltage-divider network to cause the base to be forward-biased by the amount
$$-9(1000)/(1000 + 560) = -1.36 \text{ V}.$$
The 68-Ω emitter resistor causes the base to get some feedback

voltage but does not influence our procedure. With the voltage on, we can check to see if the base voltage is negative (between −0.5 and −1.36 V). If the voltage is not negative, we should first check the 1-kΩ and 5600-Ω resistors. If these resistors are found to be working properly, the transistor base-emitter junction is defective, and we must replace the transistor (assuming no input signal is applied to the circuit).

We should next check the emitter voltage of the transistor. The best we can say about the emitter voltage is that it should be at least a few tenths of a volt positive with respect to the base voltage. If the emitter voltage is about −9 V (the battery voltage), we should suspect that the 100-μF capacitor is defective. The collector voltage should be between −5 and −9 V, depending upon the primary resistance of the collector transformer; the higher the resistance, the lower the collector voltage. This test will show if the collector transformer is defective. If we know the resistance of the primary winding of the collector transformer, say 500 Ω, and we get an indication of −9 V of collector voltage, we should suspect either a shorted 0.1−μF capacitor across the primary winding or a very low gain in the transistor.

These are all the useful voltage checks we can make. Since the voltage checks made on this circuit are equally as informative as the resistance checks performed on the previous circuits in this chapter, a final check consists of unsoldering the transistor and checking it with the beta-checker. The beta-checker indicates the value of transistor gain and leakage and, if nothing else, eliminates the transistor as the cause of circuit failure. An ohmmeter and a capacitance-bridge component check make the troubleshooting of this circuit complete.

TROUBLESHOOTING THE VOLTAGE AMPLIFIER

The voltage amplifier, shown in Fig. 5–7, illustrates a technique called *bias stabilization*. The 200-kΩ, 20-kΩ, and 200-Ω

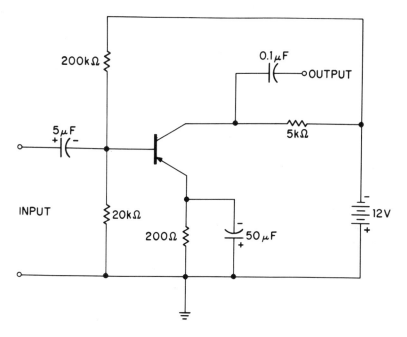

Fig. 5-7. Voltage amplifier.

resistors compensate for normal variation of transistor parameters, which would otherwise tend to change the bias and
operating point. The 200-Ω emitter resistor serves the same
purpose as the cathode resistor; it provides negative feedback
to stabilize the bias point.

We begin troubleshooting by disconnecting the input signal. We see that the transistor is biased on by the voltage
divider consisting of the 20-kΩ and 200-kΩ resistors. The base
voltage applied to the transistor can be quickly calculated
$V_{base} = -12$ V$[20$ kΩ $/ (200$ kΩ $+ 20$ kΩ$)] = -1.09$ V. Because
the transistor has some input resistance (appearing in parallel
with the 20-kΩ resistor), the value -1.09 V is only approximate,
so we should look for a value of base voltage between about
-0.2 and -1.5 V. The base current is about 100 μA.

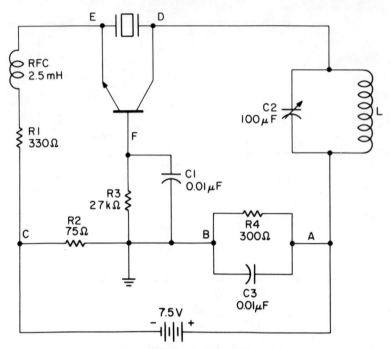

Fig. 5-8. Crystal oscillator.

The collector current (drawn through the 200-Ω emitter resistor) causes the emitter to have a slightly negative voltage with respect to ground, depending upon just how much collector current there is. If the transistor has a beta of about 20, as is typical, then we should get between 0.30 and 0.50 V (negative) of emitter voltage. This is due to a collector current of 2 mA ($I_c = \beta I_b$, $I_c = 20 \times 100 = 2$ mA).

Since the collector current is 2 mA, we know that we should get a voltage drop across the 5-kΩ load resistor of 2 mA $\times$ 5 kΩ = 10 V. The collector voltage should then be about -2 V $[-12$ V $- (-10$ V$)]$. If we find that the collector voltage is more negative than -2 V, the transistor should be checked out of circuit with the beta-checker, as the transistor gain may be very low. If the collector voltage is about 0 V, the 5-kΩ resistor may be open-circuited (burned out).

TROUBLESHOOTING THE CRYSTAL OSCILLATOR

Figure 5–8 illustrates a crystal oscillator. The RF transistor is used in a conventional collector-tuned, common-base circuit. We can begin troubleshooting by taking a few voltage readings (with the VTVM). The voltage divider, consisting of R2 and R4, should cause 6 V to be dropped across R4 (the voltmeter positive lead on A and the negative lead on B) and 1.5 V to be dropped across R2 (the voltmeter positive lead on B and the negative lead on C). These indications tell us if resistors R2 and R4 are good. Resistors R2 and R4 are important because they establish emitter bias and collector bias, respectively. If resistor R2 opened up, we would expect to read 7.5 V across R4 (the voltmeter positive lead on A and the negative lead on B). If capacitor C3 shorted, we would read 7.5 V across R2. If this circuit were working, we would get a voltage drop of a few tenths of a volt from the emitter (positive lead of VTVM) to the base (negative lead of VTVM). We can check the collector voltage between D and B. If coil L is good, we should read 6 V, with the positive VTVM lead on D and the negative VTVM lead on B. We should also get an indication of 1.5 V from point B (positive VTVM lead) to point E (negative VTVM lead). This checks R1 and the radio frequency choke (RFC) for continuity.

After we disconnect the battery, we can perform a few resistance checks. If we place the ohmmeter positive lead on F and the negative lead on E, we should read the forward-biased resistance of the transistor base-emitter junction. This resistance should be about 100 Ω. If we reverse the ohmmeter leads, we should get an indication of no less than about 27 kΩ (27 kΩ is the value of R3). An indication of less than 27 kΩ would indicate either a shorted capacitor C1 or a defective transistor, because the reverse-biased, emitter-base junction of the transistor should have a resistance of much greater than 50 kΩ.

The next measurement to perform is of the forward and reverse-biased resistances of the collector-base transistor junctions. If we place the positive ohmmeter lead on F and the negative ohmmeter lead on D, we should read a resistance of 100 Ω or so. An indication of less than 100 Ω could only mean that C1 is shorted, since when C1 shorts, a 300-Ω indication in R4 appears in parallel with the junction resistance of 100 Ω. If we reverse the ohmmeter leads, we will again read a resistance of about 27 kΩ. If C1 has been eliminated as a source of trouble, then a resistance of less than 27 kΩ can only mean a defective transistor.

Usually, an oscillator is designed to operate only if the transistor meets a certain gain requirement (*e.g.*, beta equals 20). For values of gain less than the necessary gain, the circuit will not operate. For this reason, it is a good idea to check the dc transistor gain with the beta-checker. In any case, the transistor should be removed from the circuit to take more accurate reverse-biased checks with the ohmmeter. The best way to check the crystal is to replace it with a known good crystal.

After replacing the defective component we should, of course, perform some of these circuit checks again to insure that we did not make an error in the process of reconnecting the circuit.

TROUBLESHOOTING THE OR CIRCUIT

Figure 5-9 illustrates a transistor OR gate with labeled test points. Transistor-gating circuitry is easy to check, usually, because the transistor is usually on or off, not oscillating or amplifying. The easiest way to check this OR gate is to supply a negative signal (voltage) at A or B. A negative voltage at A or B will cause the output D to approach ground potential. Any voltage greater than about 0 V at both inputs A and B will cause the voltage at D to be at 9 V, because the transistor is cut off in this case.

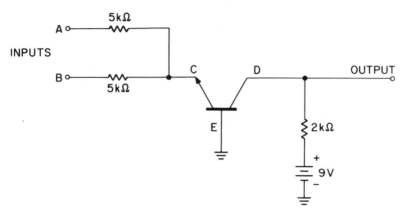

Fig. 5-9. Transistor OR gate.

If we disconnect the battery (and inputs A and B), we can check the forward-biased resistance of the transistor base-emitter junction by placing the ohmmeter positive lead on E and the negative lead on C. If we do not get an indication of about 100 Ω, we should naturally suspect that the transistor is defective. Similarly, if we reverse the ohmmeter leads, reverse-biasing the base-emitter junction, we should get an indication of much greater than 50 kΩ. An indication of a lower resistance means that the transistor is defective.

If we now disconnect the output-signal line so that there are no external circuit influences, we can check the base-collector junction forward-biased (the ohmmeter positive lead on E and the negative lead on D) and reverse-biased (performed by reversing the ohmmeter leads). The forward-biased resistance should be about 100 Ω and the reverse-biased resistance should be in excess of 50 kΩ.

Since there are only three additional components to this circuit, a wise move would be to check the three resistors next. As a final check the transistor should have its gain checked in the beta-checker or similar test instrument. Of course, after replacing any component, these checks should be made again to prevent a premature transistor or component failure.

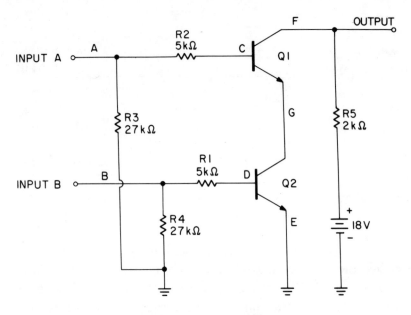

Fig. 5-10. Transistor AND gate.

TROUBLESHOOTING THE AND CIRCUIT

Figure 5-10 illustrates a transistor AND gate. Although we can check this with an ohmmeter, a quicker way to trouble-shoot this circuit is with a dry cell of about 1.5 V and a volt-meter. We should start by connecting the negative terminal of the dry cell to ground E. When we place the positive battery terminal on B, the voltage at D should be about 0.5 V, because transistor Q2 should be conducting. If the voltage at D is not slightly positive, either R1 or Q2 is defective. If we place a 10-kΩ resistor from B to D and find that the voltage indicated at D is still not about 0.5 V, the transistor should be replaced. If the voltage at D is about 1.5 V, then transistor Q2 is not functioning properly; the base-emitter junction would cause this, indicating that Q2 is defective.

The next step is to check Q1 in the same manner. If we place the positive terminal of the dry cell on A (the negative terminal should still be on E), we should get an indication of about 0.5 V from point C to point G, if we ground G (this checks the base-emitter junction of Q1). An indication of about 0 V probably means that R2 is open. An indication of about 1.5 V from C to G (with G still grounded) means that Q1 is probably defective (its base-emitter junction is open-circuited).

Now, unground test point G and connect test points A and B together and to the dry-cell positive terminal. This forward-biases both transistors. With Q2 forward-biased, test point G should be about 0.3 V with respect to test point G. Improper voltage indications mean that the transistor being tested is defective and should be replaced. This presupposes that resistor R5 has been checked and found good, because if R5 is defective, neither transistor can be checked by this method.

Although resistors R3 and R4 do not appreciably influence circuit operation, they should be checked after all previous checks have been made (check R3 and R4 with an ohmmeter).

TROUBLESHOOTING THE VOLTAGE REGULATOR

Figure 5-11 is an illustration of a voltage regulator. The transistor voltage regulator illustrated uses shunt transistors to obtain an output regulated to within 0.5 per cent. If we leave the voltage input connected to the circuit, the voltage at A should be about 28 V. If the circuit is malfunctioning, begin troubleshooting by disconnecting the Q1 emitter from ground. Next, check the dc voltage from A to D (with the positive VTVM lead on A and the negative lead on D). The voltage indicated should be 27 V, as this is the reference voltage established by CR1 (CR1 is a voltage-reference or zener diode).

If the voltage indication is not 27 V, disconnect the base of Q2 from D. Take a voltage reading from A to D again, and if the voltage is still not 27 V, disconnect the input to the circuit and test R1 with an ohmmeter, since if R1 is defective, no voltage will be present at A.

If R1 is working properly (28 Ω), check R2 with an ohmmeter. R2 serves the purpose of loading diode CR1 (in the absence of transistor loading), and if R2 fails, the voltage across CR1 will be 0 V with the Q2 base disconnected from D. If R2 is found to be functioning properly, then CR1 is defective.

If the voltage indication is 27 V, with the Q2 base disconnected from D, then one of the transistors (or both) is defective. Begin checking by disconnecting the Q1 emitter from ground and by disconnecting the Q1 base from the Q2 emitter and then reconnect the Q2 emitter to ground. This leaves only transistor Q2 connected. Reconnect the Q2 base to D. Since this circuit is not supplying a high current to an output circuit (the output circuit should be disconnected), transistor Q2 should be capable of handling the regulating requirements of the circuit by itself.

Recheck the voltage from A to D again, with the positive VTVM lead on A and the negative VTVM lead on D. An indication of less than 27 V means that Q2 is defective. If we get an indication of 27 V, then Q1 must be defective, since it is the only component left that has not been checked and could account for a nonfunctioning circuit. Replace the defective component and perform the checks again to prevent a costly failure resulting from a mistaken evaluation.

TROUBLESHOOTING THE PREAMPLIFIER

Now that we have gained some experience at troubleshooting transistor circuits, it is time to troubleshoot a typical piece of transistor equipment—the preamplifier. Any piece of electronic equipment is no more difficult to troubleshoot than its parts. As a matter of fact, the only difference between

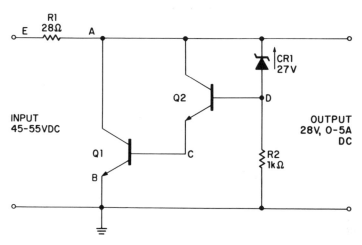

Fig. 5-11. Voltage regulator.

troubleshooting an amplifier circuit and a preamplifier unit is the amount of time expended.

We can troubleshoot the preamplifier illustrated in Fig. 5-12 in several ways. Probably the easiest way to troubleshoot this circuit is with an oscilloscope and an audio generator. The next easiest way to troubleshoot this circuit is with the VTVM and beta-checker, commercial or otherwise. The most time-consuming method of troubleshooting this circuit is with just an ohmmeter. This is not to say that an ohmmeter would not be useful when troubleshooting this circuit with an oscilloscope and an audio generator; it just means that if we troubleshoot this circuit with no other aid than an ohmmeter (and perhaps a beta-checker), we will be wasting an appreciable amount of time.

To demonstrate this fact, we will troubleshoot this circuit in three ways—with the oscilloscope and audio generator as our primary tools, with the VTVM as our primary tool, and with the ohmmeter as our primary tool. Since we chose the preamplifier as a typical unit, there is no reason to suspect that

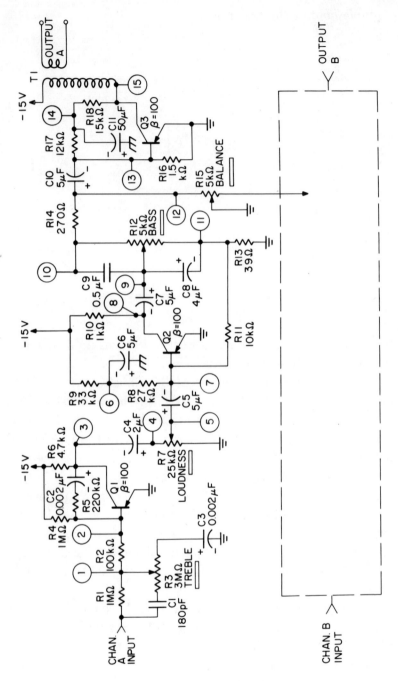

Fig. 5-12. Preamplifier.

troubleshooting any other piece of transistor equipment would be more difficult if we have the right tools and methods (procedure).

The preamplifier has two units, which are exactly identical in circuitry. These units are the circuitry for the channel A and channel B amplifiers. The only interconnection between these units, besides power-supply connections, is the "balance" potentiometer. Dual-gauged potentiometers (treble, loudness, and bass) might be used. Double-section switches may also be used for switching the inputs and outputs. Unless there is a power-supply failure, then most likely only one channel pre-amplifier will be malfunctioning. Figure 5-12 illustrates just the channel A preamplifier since the channel B preamplifier is identical. The first thing to determine, then, is which channel preamplifier is nonoperative. This can usually be determined immediately. We will assume that the channel A preamplifier is defective, which is why the channel A preamplifier schematic is shown. We begin troubleshooting at this point with power-supply checks so that we can troubleshoot the amplifier cir-cuitry using the preamplifier power supplies. Any defects in the preamplifier power supplies should be corrected before beginning the preamplifier troubleshooting.

TROUBLESHOOTING THE PREAMPLIFIER USING THE OSCILLOSCOPE AND AUDIO GENERATOR

The best way to troubleshoot this circuit is to break it into *blocks,* a block in this case being a transistor stage. We set the audio generator for a frequency of about 1000 cps (cycles per second) with an amplitude of several volts and connect it to the channel A input. The oscilloscope should be on ac and should use the audio generator for a triggering source. Actually, we want just enough audio input to drive Q1 without a distorted output. Since Q1 has a gain (specified by the manufacturer) of 100 and since, in respect to dc, the transistor is biased to draw about 1.5 mA of collector current according to which Ic is about equal to $(-15 \text{ V}/\text{Rb}) \times 100 = -1500/\text{R4} = -1500/1 \text{ M}\Omega = 1.5 \text{ mA}$, we should supply enough of an input to get the collector current to vary by ± 0.5 mA. This means we have to supply a base current of $\pm 0.5 \text{ mA}/100 = \pm 5 \mu\text{A}$. Since the input is connected to the base through R1 and R2 (1.1 MΩ), it will take at least a volt of input to get the required output (not too small, not distorted) at test point 3 (the Q1 collector).

The output at test point 3, as observed on the oscilloscope, should have a peak-to-peak amplitude of about 5 V (centered on a line at about 7.5 V of collector voltage if viewed with the oscilloscope on dc). If we do not get a sine-wave indication at test point 3, we should disconnect R2 from the base of Q1 and measure the voltage at test point 2 (the open end of R2). We disconnect the base of Q1 from R2 to make our test point 2 measurement easier. When the probe is on test point 2, there should be indicated on the oscilloscope a sine wave with a peak-to-peak amplitude of at least 1 V. If we do not get this indication, then R1 and R2 should be checked.

If R1 and R2 are found to be functioning properly and we do not get the proper indication at test point 3, transistor Q1 or resistors R4 and/or R6 are defective. Shut off the power and check components R4 and R6 with an ohmmeter (after disconnecting one end of each resistor from the circuit) and then check Q1 with the ohmmeter and with the beta-checker, as described earlier in this chapter. Remember that all transistors in this circuit are pnp transistors.

After these components have been checked and the defective one replaced, we should be able to obtain the correct indication at test point 3 (after reconnecting the circuit). Now trace the sine-wave signal to test points 4 and 5 with the oscilloscope probe. We should get a 5-V peak-to-peak sine wave at test point 4; if we do not, C4 must be replaced. With the loudness potentiometer at about mid-range, we should get an indication of a sine wave at test point 5 with a peak-to-peak amplitude of about 1 V. If we do not get this indication, we then disconnect the base of Q2 from C5. Check test point 5 again; this time we should get a voltage of 2.5 V peak-to-peak (because the Q2 base-emitter junction is not in parallel with about 12.5 kΩ of the loudness potentiometer anymore; the resistance of the conducting base-emitter junction is about 2 kΩ). If we do not now get a voltage of about 2.5 V peak-to-peak, replace R7.

Now, with the Q2 base still disconnected from C5, check the signal at the open end of C5 (negative). This signal should also be a 2.5-V peak-to-peak sine wave. If not, replace C5. We should now reconnect the base of Q2 to C5. Check the voltage at test point 5 again; it should be a sine wave with a peak-to-peak amplitude of about 1 V. If we observe an abnormal indication, we then disconnect C7 from the collector of Q2. This will eliminate transistor-loading effects at the Q2 input. If we still do not get a 2.5-V peak-to-peak indication at test point 5, we must check components R8, R9, R10, and C6. Then Q2 should be checked with an ohmmeter and a beta-checker (beta should be about 100 from the manufacturer's information).

After replacing the defective component, we are able to obtain the correct indication at test point 5. Reconnect the collector of Q2 to C7 (negative). Because of the feedback network consisting mainly of R11 and the base-boost network consisting of C8, C9, R12, and R13, we should expect an output at test point 8 not much in excess of the output observed at test point 3. We should look for an output of between 5 and 10 V peak to peak at test point 8. The problem here is that if we do not get this output, because of the complicated coupling network to Q3, troubleshooting the remaining portion of the circuit will take quite some time.

We can simplify the problem somewhat if we disconnect C10 (negative) from the rest of the circuit. This eliminates the loading effect of Q3. If the output at test point 8 is still low, we must disconnect R14 from R15. If the output at test point 8 is correct, R15 is either defective or improperly adjusted. If the output at test point 8 is still not within the range of 5 to 10 V peak to peak (Vpp), check the components of the base-boost network—C8, C9, R11, R12, and R13. After replacing the defective component, we should be able to trace the sine wave from TP8 (5–10 Vpp) to TP9 (3–8 Vpp) to TP11 (2–4 Vpp) to TP10 (2.5–6.5 Vpp), after reconnecting C10 (negative) and R14. These voltages were determined by using the fact that a 1-μF capacitor offers a reactance at 1000 cps of about 150 Ω and by redrawing the schematic to show the voltage dividers formed by the circuit resistors and capacitors.

Our output at TP12 should be between 2 and 5 Vpp; this indication depends to some extent on the setting of R15, so R15 should be set about midway when taking this reading. If we do not get the proper indication at TP12, we must check C10, C11, R16–R18, T1, and Q3. The reason we check these components as a group is that an improper indication at TP12 is caused by improper loading of the Q3 circuit (the rest of the components have been checked). This completes the troubleshooting procedure. If our defective component were somewhere in the Q3 circuit, then the oscilloscope got us to this point in less than five minutes, because our other indications, up to the TP12 indication, were correct.

Checking the Q3 circuit is best done with an ohmmeter (after disconnecting the power) and with the beta-checker with Q3 out of circuit.

TROUBLESHOOTING THE PREAMPLIFIER USING THE VTVM

The disadvantage in using only a VTVM to troubleshoot a preamplifier circuit is that we do not have a dynamic test of the circuit. In other words, with no input signal supplied to the preamplifier, various components that can only be checked quickly with an ac signal have to be checked out of circuit (as with an ohmmeter) or not checked at all. In most cases, with no ac signal supplied at the preamplifier input, capacitive branches (consisting of capacitors and resistors) do not show up as being defective unless capacitors short resulting in a change in dc levels.

We begin VTVM troubleshooting by checking the voltage at the base of Q1 (test point 2). Since Q1 is biased on through R4, this voltage should be a few tenths of a volt negative. If it is not, R4 must be checked first. If we find R4 good, then Q1 must be taken out of the circuit and checked with the ohmmeter and the beta-checker. Reviewing how to check a pnp transistor with an ohmmeter, we place the positive ohmmeter lead on the emitter and the negative lead on the base. We should observe an indication of about 100 Ω. When we reverse the leads, we should get an indication in excess of 50 kΩ. Then the positive ohmmeter lead should be placed on the collector and the negative lead on the base, and we should observe an indication of about 100 Ω. When we reverse the ohmmeter leads, we should read a resistance in excess of 50 kΩ. If these conditions are not met, the transistor is defective and should be replaced.

Next we check the Q1 collector voltage (test point 3). If the Q1 gain is up to specifications, the voltage should be about 7.5 V. If we do not get this indication, we check R6. Now we check the voltage at test point 4. Since we are not supplying an ac signal input, the voltage at test point 4 should be 0 V. Any other indication would mean that capacitor C4 or C5 has shorted and should be checked. The voltage at test point 5 should be 0 V for the same reason. The voltage at test point 6 should be $-15 \text{ V} \times [27 \text{ k}\Omega/(27 \text{ k}\Omega + 33 \text{ k}\Omega)]$ or about 6.75 V, using the voltage-divider technique with resistors R8 and R9. In using this relation, we assumed that the "cold" end of R8

was at ground. Actually, the cold end of R8 is at the Q2 base
voltage which should be about -0.5 V, if Q2 is conducting as
it should be. If we get an improper indication at test point 6,
we should then check resistors R8 and R9. We should also
check capacitor C6, which, if shorted, would give us a false
reading also.

If transistor Q2 is operating properly, then the voltage at
test point 7 should be about -0.5 V, and if we do not get this
indication on the VTVM, we should assume that Q2 is defective.
After replacing Q2, if necessary, we should check the voltage
at test point 8. This voltage should be approximately -15 V
$+$Ib (base current) $\times \beta \times 1$ kΩ (R10) or -15 V $+$ (15 V/
60 kΩ) (this is the base current) $\times 100 \times 1$ k$\Omega = -15$ V $+$
25 V $= +10$ V. This is impossible. The transistor is drawing
enough current to drop the full power-supply voltage across
R10. Q2 should be very much in saturation, and the voltage at
the Q2 collector should only be a few tenths of a volt negative.
If we get, let us say, a volt or two at the collector of Q2, we
should check Q2 with the beta-checker to determine its gain.
If Q2 had a gain of 100, as it should, the collector voltage would
be almost zero. Under ac operation, the feedback resistor R11
and the base-boost network would supply enough negative feedback to Q2 to keep it out of saturation.

We should now check the voltages at test points 9, 10, 11,
and 12. The voltages at all these test points should be just
perceptively negative. If the voltages are more than slightly
negative, we should check capacitors C7, C8, C9, and C10 because if these capacitors shorted, we would get a greater
negative voltage at the test points than normal. While we are
working in this portion of the circuit, it might be wise to check
the unchecked resistors, that is, R11 through R15.

What voltage should we find at test point 14? This is not
very difficult to determine; the voltage is dependent on the
primary resistance of T1. If T1 has a primary resistance of 1 kΩ,

this is how we find the voltage. Let us call the collector voltage (at test point 15) V1. Then the base current of Q3 = V1/(15 kΩ + 12 kΩ) approximately or Ib = V1/27 kΩ. Now we have to determine what V1 should be. V1 will be equal to -15 V + Ic (collector current) $\times$ 1 kΩ. Ic = β $\times$ Ib = (100 $\times$ V1)/27 kΩ. This gives us the result V1 = -5.3 V. This is the voltage we should get at test point 15. The voltage at test point 14 is -5.3 $\times$ 12 kΩ/27 kΩ = -2.5 V. Since Q3 is conducting, the voltage at test point 13 should be slightly negative (minus a few tenths of a volt). Components C11, R16–R18, T1, and transistor Q3 should be checked, if we do not get these indications on the VTVM.

This was more difficult than troubleshooting the preamplifier with the oscilloscope, and we did not even obtain indications of how well the preamplifier was performing with an ac signal input. This shows why an audio generator and oscilloscope can be very helpful at times in troubleshooting transistor circuits.

TROUBLESHOOTING THE PREAMPLIFIER USING THE OHMMETER

Although the position of the ohmmeter in troubleshooting is an important one when circuits are as complicated as the preamplifier circuit, troubleshooting with the ohmmeter alone can be quite tedious and wasteful.

First, the transistors can only be checked for resistance. Previously, if we got an incorrect voltage indication at the base or collector, we knew, after having checked capacitors and resistors, that the transistor was defective. From a voltage indication, we knew also if the gain of a transistor were low.

To check each transistor will take about five minutes longer, using only the ohmmeter and the beta-checker. The best way to troubleshoot this circuit is to remove the transistors first, so that the other circuit resistances will not affect the transistor-resistance readings. With the transistors removed, we can also check the components with the least amount of trouble. For example, checking the resistance of R8 or R9 was complicated previously by the fact that the Q2 base-collector junction was in parallel with these resistors. A similar condition existed in the checking of resistors R17 and R18. We could, though, check these resistors with the transistors left in the circuit. For example, if we place the ohmmeter positive lead at the junction of R6 and R4 and the negative lead at the base of Q1, we would expect an indication of about 4.8 kΩ (4.7 kΩ + the forward-biased, base-collector resistance of Q1 = 100 Ω). If we reverse the ohmmeter leads, we would expect an indication of greater than 54.7 kΩ (R6 in series with the reverse-biased, base-collector resistance of Q1 equal to at least 54.7 kΩ). The base-emitter junction of Q1, having nothing in parallel with it, is easy to check. Q2 and Q3 can be checked similarly in circuit. There is little reason to leave them in the circuit, though, because later we may have to perform a gain measurement necessitating their removal.

Checking the rest of the components requires a tedious method with the ohmmeter. Each resistor and capacitor must be singly checked to determine its condition. With 18 circuit resistors and 11 circuit capacitors and no further evidence to point to which component is faulty, this is quite a time-consuming job. In summary, always determine the most efficient way to troubleshoot a circuit before undertaking the task.

CHAPTER VI

Specialized Service Information and Equipment

In order to be successful troubleshooters we must know our test equipment and must be able to select the proper instrument for the job we plan to undertake. A "tough dog" is a term used to describe a very difficult service problem. In many instances, a primary difficulty has been that the technician was not using the proper test equipment or tool, which would have made the job easy.

SERVICE BOOKS AND MAGAZINES

One should also make use of diode and transistor substitution books. These booklets readily indicate exact replacements for those hard-to-come-by diodes and transistors. One manufacturer lists 31 solid-state devices that will replace approximately 10,000 types currently in use. Another lists 12 devices that will replace more than 7500 types now in use. Substitution books and charts are continually updated. The serviceman should acquire as many as possible. If he neglects to do so, he may find himself with a backlog of uncompleted work for want of a special transistor or diode.

You should subscribe to the service magazines, because they not only give service information, but also list new products. They provide advance information on pending developments and equipment, new types of test instruments, service aids, and also a column devoted to the tackling of "tough dogs." Manufacturers avail themselves of these magazines to inform technicians in the industry of the changes, modifications, and repairs that are new in the field. Manufacturers also provide service manuals, which may be subscribed to on a yearly basis; these may be filed and held readily available for use. A variety of manufacturers also advertise in these magazines in which we might find a special new time-saving tool.

TEST EQUIPMENT

This is a list of suggested test instruments that every service bench should have.

Power Supply. This power supply (see Fig. 6–1) is specially designed for transistorized equipment. Notice that it is an adjustable power source, which is metered, so that we can tell what the current drain of the circuit under test is. This is a very desirable feature—particularly when the equipment being tested does not exhibit any clear-cut symptoms—because it points out problems due to either a low or high current drain. It is used not only as a power source when a unit is placed on the bench for repair but also as a substitute power supply when trouble is suspected in the power supply of the equipment. When substituting, if a hum, ripple, or oscillation disappears, it becomes obvious that the power supply of the equipment is to blame. Appropriate troubleshooting will determine the

Fig. 6-1. EICO Model 1025 solid-state power supply.

reasons for its improper operation. A power supply with the features of that shown or one similar to it would be desirable.

Multimeter. A multimeter (see Fig. 6–2) is essential, and one that will not load down the circuit under test is recommended. A new type of multimeter now on the market has all the advantages of a VTVM, without any of its disadvantages. This is the FET meter, which uses field-effect transistors. The transistors provide instant warm-up. Completely portable, it has minimum circuit loading of 15 MΩ input resistance on dc voltage ranges and 10 MΩ of input impedance on ac voltage ranges. These features mean that you can test any circuit without affecting its operation or loading it down. It has a zero center scale of 0.5 V for checking transistor circuits and an input frequency response that is essentially flat to 10 MHz.

Fig. 6-2. Sencore field effect meter.

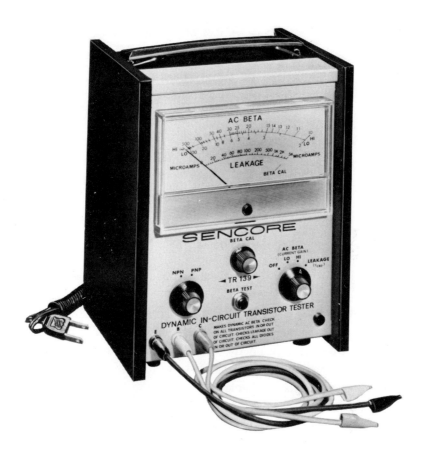

Fig. 6-3. Sencore beta tester.

An ohmmeter is built into it, and it can also be used to measure very low direct currents, important in transistor servicing. Either this kind of multitester or one with similar features should be secured.

In-circuit Transistor Checker. An in-circuit transistor and diode checker (see Fig. 6–3) is another useful piece of test equipment. The one shown here can check transistors in circuit in seconds with the use of an ac beta measurement or a leakage

Fig. 6-4. EICO Model 430 general-purpose 3-inch oscilloscope.

measurement. Provision is also made for checking diodes or rectifiers, either in or out of the circuit. Many types of transistor checkers are available on the market, and a choice should be made of the one with the best possible features. Do not compromise on a transistor checker—it can make the difference between guessing and knowing. Do not forget that the ac beta measurement is much more useful than the dc beta measurement, making one of these commercial beta-checkers more useful than the one described in the text.

Oscilloscope. Another test instrument that is considered necessary is the oscilloscope (see Fig. 6–4). An oscilloscope can be used to check circuits in a different manner from ordinary test instruments. Use the oscilloscope as a means to check distortion, the hum in power supplies, or the frequency of oscillators. It can be used to trace a signal through a chain of amplifiers or simply to check the performance of circuits. An instrument that permits a rapid check, it will aid you in pinpointing a source of trouble. The oscilloscope can also be used to measure peak-to-peak ac voltage.

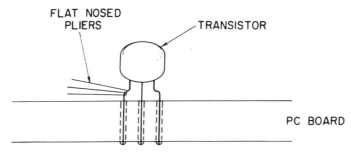

Fig. 6-5. Use of flat-nosed pliers to hold transistor being soldered to the PC board.

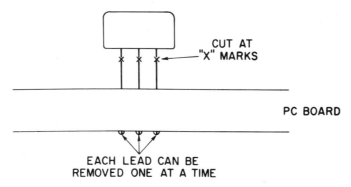

Fig. 6-6. Removing a defective component that has three or more leads.

REPAIRING PRINTED CIRCUIT BOARDS

We must emphasize the need for extreme care in the repair or replacement of components on printed circuit boards. These boards are not made to take abuse, even though they may appear to be quite strong. In soldering or unsoldering components, great care should be exercised to make sure that the etched copper strips on the PC (printed circuit) board are not damaged. Undue bending or twisting can cause one or more of these etched strips to crack, and because they have a coating, the crack may go undetected and cause problems later.

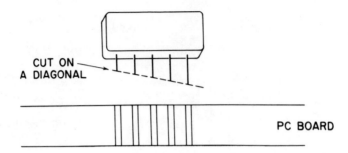

Fig. 6-7. Leads of a component cut on a diagonal.

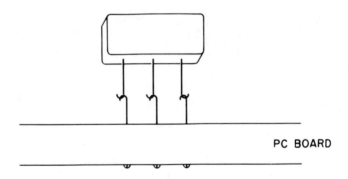

Fig. 6-8. Replacing components when there is no access to the bottom of the PC board.

Work on PC boards requires the use of special tools and hardware. A good set of tools will insure that damage to components cannot possibly be caused by slippage. A good pair of small, flat-nosed pliers may be used to hold a transistor firmly while it is being soldered to the PC board. As is shown in Fig. 6–5, this acts to block the heat of the iron from traveling up the soldered lead to the transistor and possibly damaging it permanently.

A technique used to remove a defective component that may have three or more leads is shown in Fig. 6–6. This technique prevents damage to the PC board from overheating. Cut each lead of the defective component as close to the board as possible. Then unsolder the leads from the PC board one at a time.

Before you install a component that has more than two leads, the leads should be cut on a diagonal as shown in Fig. 6–7. Much time may be wasted fumbling around in an attempt to install the leads simultaneously into their respective holes. With this method the leads can be installed one at a time, and after soldering, the excess lead lengths can be cut to one size. This is particularly helpful when replacing a module that has seven or eight leads.

Replacement of components can also be made when there is no access to the bottom side of the PC board (see Fig. 6–8). Clip the leads from the defective component and leave the leads remaining above the board. Each lead on the board is then bent into a small loop as shown. The trick here is to apply heat for as short a period of time as possible, so tin all the leads on the replacement component. Then bend them and hook them into their respective loops. It only takes a moment to hold the soldering iron to the loop and have the solder melt into it. Be careful not to hold the iron on too long, since the heat will travel down the lead and may cause it to become unsoldered from the PC board. Some new types of manufactured solder connectors (see Fig. 6–9) also make soldering fast and easy. Place the lead from the replacement component into the connector, apply heat, and solder.

Handling a break in a PC board is quite easy. First, scrape off the coating over the etched copper strip either by using a solvent made for this purpose or by using a fine wire brush, working it back and forth across the break until the copper strip shines. Then, tin the copper strip on both sides of the crack,

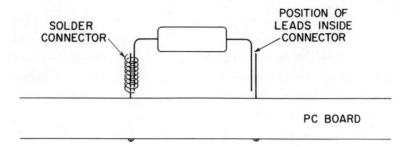

Fig. 6-9. Manufactured solder connector in use.

place the iron right on the crack, add solder, and melt it across the crack. If you would like to improve on this, add a flexible wire across the crack before the final soldering is done. This will prevent the strip from cracking again, even though the board may be flexed. If you discover a break in the board by the use of an ohmmeter and cannot find it, repair it by placing an insulated wire between the two points to which your meter was connected, tinning both ends, and then soldering them down. This will take care of the break and save a great deal of time trying to locate it.

When removing leads from the PC board, it is often difficult to clean out the holes, which may have become clogged with solder. This usually happens when unsoldering leads from the PC board, and it too is easy to correct. All we need to do is place a round-pointed, wood toothpick over the hole to be cleaned. Apply the iron lightly to the bottom of the hole, and the toothpick will drop down into it. Solder will not stick to wood, of course, so the toothpick is the best soldering aid for this chore.

When a transistor mounted in a heat sink needs replacement, it is very important to use a silicon grease between the replacement transistor and the heat sink. The transistor can be ruined if the internal heat generated by it cannot be transferred away from it. That is the purpose of the heat sink, but the contact between it and the case of the transistor must be of very low thermal resistance, so that it will not impede the flow of heat away from it. The heat sink will dissipate the heat if a good thermal contact is made, and the silicon grease is made for that purpose.

We hope that the hints and bits of information given in this chapter will add to your knowledge and help you to service solid-state devices successfully.

Index

172